X-PLANES

AND PROTOTYPES

X–PLANES

AND PROTOTYPES

FROM NAZI SECRET WEAPONS TO THE WARPLANES OF THE FUTURE

Jim Winchester

BARNES
& NOBLE
BOOKS

NEW YORK

Copyright © 2005 Amber Books Ltd

This edition published by Barnes & Noble, Inc.,
by arrangement with Amber Books Ltd
2005 Barnes & Noble Books

M 10 9 8 7 6 5 4 3 2 1

ISBN: 0-7607-7091-3

Editorial and design by
Amber Books Ltd
Bradley's Close
74–77 White Lion Street
London N1 9PF
www.amberbooks.co.uk

Project Editor: James Bennett
Picture Research: James Hollingworth
Design: EQ Media

Printed in Singapore

CONTENTS

INTRODUCTION

'X' stands for the unknown in mathematics and physics. An 'X-Plane' is an experimental or research aircraft, designed to explore the unknown boundaries of aerodynamics, powerplant technologies or materials science. The term 'X-plane', has gone beyond its narrow US definition to become shorthand for a research aircraft or technology demonstrator of any origin.

Beyond the California desert, the industries of many other countries, notably Britain, France, Germany and the USSR, created some remarkable research aircraft and technically interesting prototypes, including vertical take-off aeroplanes and experimental rotorcraft.

The US Air Force Flight Test Center's motto is 'Toward the Unknown'. The golden age of rocket aircraft and heroic test pilots at Edwards Air Force Base from 1947 to 1975 was an exciting era that captured the public's imagination, and was

Above: *In 1903 Orville and Wilbur Wright flew the first ever 'X-plane', the Wright Flyer.*

celebrated in fiction, film, comics and models hanging from the ceilings of millions of bedrooms.

This volume concerns itself only with manned (or in current parlance, inhabited) vehicles. Pilotless rotorcraft predated manned helicopters by a decade, however, and half of the US X-series aircraft have been unmanned rockets, aerodynamic shapes or Uninhabited Air Vehicles (UAVs). But while these have contributed greatly to aerospace research, they lack the elements of human risk and popular appeal of manned aircraft.

X-planes are by no means exclusively military. In just over a century, civilian engineers and test pilots have advanced aeronautics from the tentative hops of the Wright Flyer to beyond the atmosphere with the SpaceshipOne, and are certain to go higher, faster and further.

HIGHER, FASTER, FURTHER

The quest for aircraft that could outperform their contemporaries has mainly been the result of military necessity. It has also been a source of national pride for those countries with strong aircraft industries, particularly the US, UK, France and the USSR. The 1950s in particular saw absolute speed records broken with regularity and the milestones of Mach 1, 2 and 3 fall to US Air Force and Navy rocket planes flying out of Edwards Air Force Base in California. In the following decade the X-15 extended the manned aircraft flight envelope through Mach 4, 5 and 6. Most of these aircraft had to be dropped from converted bombers to save their precious fuel for the speed run and as such were impractical as the basis for warplanes.

Purpose-built aircraft designed for extreme long range and for extended high-altitude flight are rarer than pure speed machines. Notable examples of distance record breakers include the Fairey Long Range Monoplane and Rutan Voyager. Designer Burt Rutan has probably done more than any one person to extend the boundaries of flight. With the SpaceshipOne he has designed a purely civilian craft able to take passengers into space.

Left: *The fastest manned aircraft ever built, the North American X-15 reached Mach 6.72 (7297km/h or 4534mph) in 1967.*

AVRO CF-105 ARROW (1958)

Seeking a supersonic replacement for the then-new CF-100 Canuck, Avro Canada began work on a supersonic successor in 1953. On 25 March 1958 Jan Zurakowski flew the first CF-105 Arrow Mk 1. The flight test programme proceeded quickly, with five prototypes flying within a year and demonstrating near Mach 2 performance and a ceiling of over 15,240m (50,000ft). Despite these successes, the idea that missiles would be more effective and cheaper than manned interceptors took hold in Canada, as it had in Britain. On 20 February 1959, a day dubbed 'Black Friday', the project was cancelled by the government. All 10 complete or partly complete airframes were ordered destroyed, as were tools, jigs and engines. The Canadian aerospace industry never quite recovered. The BOMARC missiles that were to provide air defence were short-lived, and since then Canada has bought US fighters.

SPECIFICATIONS (first aircraft)

CREW:	two
POWERPLANT:	two 82.29kN (18,500lb-thrust) Pratt & Whitney J75-P-3 turbojet engines
MAX SPEED:	2104km/h (1307mph) (Mach 1.98)
MAX ALTITUDE:	over 15,240m (50,000ft)
SPAN:	15.24m (50ft)
LENGTH:	23.72m (77ft 10in)
HEIGHT:	6.48m (21ft 3in)
WEIGHT:	maximum 31,118kg (68,602lb)

The Arrow was one of the largest fighter aircraft ever built, and the Mk 2 would have been one of the most formidable warplanes of the 1960s. Like the TSR.2, however, it was cancelled after great expense and effort had been expended.

The prototype Arrows were powered by Pratt & Whitney J75 engines, but it was planned to use the Canadian PS-13 Iroquois with 115.7kN (26,000lb-thrust) in the Mk 2 version.

The Mk 2 would have been armed with eight Sparrow 2 medium-range missiles in a large internal weapons bay. The weapons radar was integrated with a jamming and countermeasures system.

The Arrow had a very early fly-by-wire system and used artificial feedback to the controls. It could also be flown from the ground using a datalink.

Today only one nose section, an engine and a non-flying replica of the huge Arrow project survive.

BAC.221 (1964)

In 1958, with the Fairey Delta 2 programme winding down, it was decided to extend it into a new phase by fitting an ogee wing and other features planned for the British supersonic transport project. This had evolved into the Anglo-French Concorde by the time Godfrey Auty first flew it on 1 May 1964. Conversion work was given to Bristol, soon a part of the British Aircraft Corporation (BAC). Manufacturer's trials and modifications delayed handover to the customer, the RAE at Bedford, until May 1966, by which time the first Concorde was under construction. Much of the test flying was undertaken out of Cazaux, near Bordeaux, France, due to better weather and less restricted airspace. Research flights continued into 1973, four years after the first Concorde flight, before eventual retirement to the Royal Navy's Fleet Air Arm Museum.

SPECIFICATIONS

CREW:	one
POWERPLANT:	one 62.28kN (14,000lb-thrust) Rolls-Royce RA.28R Avon afterburning turbojet engine
MAX SPEED:	1706km/h (1060mph)
MAX ALTITUDE:	unknown
SPAN:	7.62m (25ft 0in)
LENGTH:	17.55m (57ft 7in)
HEIGHT:	3.45m (11ft 4in)
WEIGHT:	unknown

Due to limited funding, which caused delays in the first flight, and differences between the BAC.221's wing and Concorde's, the 221 made less than the hoped-for contribution to the SST.

The 221's wing was similar in general shape to Concorde's, but lacked the twist, camber, droop and thickness/chord ratio. The flying control layout was also different.

The Fairey Delta 2 was highly modified to create the BAC.221, receiving an all-new wing, a longer fuselage and a taller undercarriage. The droop-snoot nose was retained from the FD.2.

Because it could not explore the high-speed handling of Concorde, the BAC.221 was mainly used for approach and landing tests, for which the long gear legs and hinged nose proved particularly suitable.

BAC (ENGLISH ELECTRIC) TSR.2 (1964)

The TSR.2 (Tactical Strike and Reconnaissance) was an ambitious programme to develop a deep-penetration reconnaissance and attack aircraft that would fly most of its mission below an altitude of 61m (200ft). To this end a sophisticated terrain following radar and navigation system was developed. After many delays Roland Beamont flew the first TSR.2 XR219 on its maiden flight on 27 September 1964. A total of 24 largely successful flights were made. On 6 April 1965, the day the second aircraft was due to fly, the project was cancelled in favour of the American F-111K, which never materialized. Six further aircraft were partially completed and mostly wound up on a weapons range. Two complete aircraft survive: XR222 at Duxford in Cambridgeshire and XR220 at Cosford in Shropshire.

SPECIFICATIONS

CREW:	two
POWERPLANT:	two 87.19kN (19,600lb-thrust) Bristol Olympus 22R afterburning turbojet engines
MAX SPEED:	Mach 2.05
MAX ALTITUDE:	over 18,288m (60,000ft)
SPAN:	11.30m (37ft 2in)
LENGTH:	27.14m (89ft 1in)
HEIGHT:	7.25m (23ft 9in)
WEIGHT:	loaded 43,500kg (95,900lb)

Many aspects of the TSR.2's design, including structures, avionics and powerplants, broke new ground. Some of this work eventually contributed to the Tornado, but the TSR.2's cancellation was a huge blow to the UK aerospace industry.

The undercarriage was a complex design and gave many problems, especially with vibrations after landing. On one occasion the TSR.2 had to land with the mainwheel bogies in the vertical position.

During ground testing and flight testing beneath a Vulcan bomber, the Olympus 320X engines intended for the TSR.2 exploded on three occasions. The first TSR.2 flight was made with restricted maximum power as the safety was considered marginal.

An internal weapons bay would have carried six 454kg (1000lb) bombs, a reconnaissance package or a nuclear weapon. Additional weapons and fuel tanks could have been carried on the wing pylons.

BELL X-1 (1946)

In 1944 the National Advisory Committee on Aeronautics (NACA) and the USAAF began a programme to explore flight in the transonic region up to and beyond Mach 1, the so-called 'sound barrier'. Bell built three XS-1 (experimental, sonic) craft, usually known as X-1s. The first X-1 made its first gliding flight from a B-29 bomber on 25 January 1946. The pilot was Jack Woolams. Powered flight tests began in December. Charles E. 'Chuck' Yeager began the Air Force test programme in June 1947 and on 14 October 1947 took 46-062, which he named 'Glamorous Glennis' after his wife, to Mach 1.06 at an altitude of 13,716m (43,000ft), becoming the first pilot to officially exceed the speed of sound. The programme carried on until July 1951, and between them the three X-1s made 151 flights.

SPECIFICATIONS

CREW:	one
POWERPLANT:	one 26.69kN (6000lb-thrust) Reaction Motors XLR-11-RM-3 rocket engine
MAX SPEED:	Mach 1.45 (1445km/h/960mph)
MAX ALTITUDE:	21,916m (71,902ft)
SPAN:	8.53m (28ft 0in)
LENGTH:	9.41m (30ft 11in)
HEIGHT:	3.31m (10ft 10in)
WEIGHT:	loaded 6691kg (14,751lb)

The X-1 began the golden era of rocket and jet aircraft designed for pure research. Its success led to a second generation of larger straight-winged X-1s, establishing the X-plane series that continues to the present day.

The secret of the X-1's ability to pass through Mach 1.0 was its all-flying tailplane, which allowed accurate trimming as the shockwave moved along the fuselage.

The XLR-11) rocket was used in several generations of X-plane. It was fuelled by an ethyl alcohol/water mix and liquid oxygen.

The fuselage shape of the X-1 was based on that of a 12.7mm (.50-calibre) bullet because that was a shape known to go supersonic with ease.

The first X-1 is at the National Air and Space Museum in Washington D.C., the second was converted to X-1E configuration and is on display at NASA Dryden. The third was destroyed in a ground explosion.

BELL X-1A, B AND D (1951)

The 'second generation' X-1 family was developed to carry on research past the speed of Mach 2, building on the work of the original X-1s. All three aircraft were very similar in shape; the X-1A and B were for dynamic stability trials and the X-1D (the X-1C was cancelled) was to explore airframe heating.

Jean 'Skip' Ziegler made the first glide flight of the X-1A on 14 February 1953. The X-1B flew on 24 September 1954, flown by Jack Ridley. One wild X-1A flight by Chuck Yeager proved the existence of the phenomenon of roll-coupling, and this aircraft was later flown to a record 27,566m (90,440ft). On 8 August 1955 it blew up on board the B-50 mothership and was jettisoned to destruction. The same fate had befallen the X-1D in August 1951, only a month after its first flight on 24 July.

SPECIFICATIONS (X-1A)

CREW:	one
POWERPLANT:	one 26.69kN (6000lb-thrust) Reaction Motors XLR-11-RM-6 rocket engine
MAX SPEED:	2655km/h (1650mph)
MAX ALTITUDE:	27,432m (90,000ft)
SPAN:	8.53m (28ft 0in)
LENGTH:	10.85m (35ft 7in)
HEIGHT:	3.25m (10ft 8in)
WEIGHT:	loaded 7,525kg (16,590lb)

The X-1B contributed to the development of control systems for winged aircraft approaching the outer limits of the atmosphere. Due to explosions and other incidents, none of the series actually reached Mach 2.

The stall characteristics of the X-1s often led to hard landings. The X-1D suffered one nosegear collapse and the X-1B had two, one of which befell future astronaut Neil Armstrong.

Later in its 27-flight career, the X-1B was fitted with reaction control nozzles in the wingtips for use at high altitude where ailerons were useless. In the event these were never flown, but were transferred to the NF-104.

Two of the three second-generation X-1s were destroyed by explosions resulting from a chemical reaction between liquid oxygen and organic seals. The only survivor, the X-1B, is displayed at the USAF National Museum in Ohio.

BELL X-2 (1952)

The X-2 was essentially an enlarged, swept-wing X-1. The second X-2 built was ready first, but was lost when it exploded under the fuselage of its B-50 carrier plane after only three test flights, the first on 27 June 1952. Test pilot Skip Zeigler and B-50 observer Frank Wolko were killed. The remaining X-2, 46-674 began test flights in August 1954 and made 10 successful supersonic and Mach 2 test flights, setting an unofficial altitude record of 38466m (126,200ft) on 7 September 1956. On 27 September of the same year 46-674 went out of control, having set an unofficial absolute record of Mach 3.196 (3370km/h, 2094mph). Test pilot Mel Apt, who was on his first X-2 flight, jettisoned the nose capsule, but was killed when it hit the desert floor before he could jump clear and open his parachute.

SPECIFICATIONS

CREW:	one
POWERPLANT:	one 66.72kN (15,000lb-thrust) Curtiss-Wright XLR25 rocket motor
MAX SPEED:	3369km/h (2094mph)
SPAN:	9.83m (32ft 3in)
LENGTH:	13.84m (45ft 5in)
HEIGHT:	3.58m (11ft 9in)
WEIGHT:	11,284kg (24,910lb)

Apart from two record-breaking flights, the ill-fated X-2 programme could be regarded as something of a failure, with the loss of both aircraft and three lives.

The X-2 had a cumbersome escape system involving detaching the nose, then manually bailing out. This system's failure saw a return to ejection seats for future X-craft.

The explosion that destroyed the second X-2 (46-675) was attributed to the reaction of liquid oxygen and the organic compound Ulmer leather, which had also claimed two of the X-1 series.

The X-2 had an unusual undercarriage arrangement with a conventional nose gear, but a retracting skid under the mid section. This was chosen because the fuselage had no room in which to retract conventional wheeled gear.

BELL XP-59A AIRACOMET (1942)

Following observation of the Gloster E.28/39, USAAF General 'Hap' Arnold ordered US industry to develop a jet aircraft with all haste. Bell was commissioned to build the airframe, while General Electric was to produce copies of the Whittle jet engine.

The one-off XP-59A used two original Whittle W.2B turbojets, and Robert Stanley became the first American jet pilot on 1 October 1942. The low-powered engines ensured that the performance hardly challenged that of the P-47 or P-51 propeller-driven fighters. A series of 13 improved YP-59s was ordered and in all 64 Airacomets were built, although they were used only for training personnel in jet operations. The Bell XP-59A clocked up a total of 59 hours and 55 minutes of flying time. It was earmarked for preservation in 1945 and has been on display at the Smithsonian National Air and Space Museum in Washington DC since 1976.

SPECIFICATIONS

CREW:	one or two
POWERPLANT:	two 5.56kN (1250lb thrust) General Electric I-A turbojet engines
MAX SPEED:	628km/h (390mph)
MAX ALTITUDE:	unknown
SPAN:	14.93m (49ft 0in)
LENGTH:	11.83m (38ft 10in)
HEIGHT:	3.76m (12ft 4in)
WEIGHT:	3320kg (7320lb) empty

America's first jet aircraft, the XP-59A, was limited in its performance and no version saw operational service. Nevertheless it did introduce many pilots and mechanics to jet engines and jet flight.

In order to conceal the nature of the XP-59A, a dummy propeller was fitted when the aircraft was on the ground and removed before take-off.

It was felt that an observer was needed to note instrument readings during flight. A rudimentary second cockpit was installed in the gun bay ahead of the pilot's cockpit soon after the first flight.

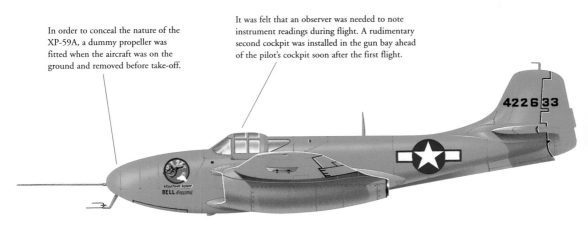

Total Airacomet production was one XP-59A, 13 YP-59As, 20 P-59As and 30 P-59Bs. The production aircraft were armed with a 37mm (1.46in) cannon and three 0.50in (12.7mm) machine guns.

BREGUET BR.1001 TAON (1957)

The Breguet Taon ('gadfly' or 'horsefly') was designed to meet a NATO tactical fighter requirement optimized for highest speed at low level, high roll manoeuvrability and short landing and take-off distances. Of the competing proposals, which included the Avro 727, Ambrosini Aerfer Ariete, Dassault Etendard IV, Folland Gnat, Fiat G.91 and Sud-Est Baroudeur, the Taon was ranked first in a 1953 NATO 'paper' evaluation. Wind tunnel tests showed the value of 'area-ruling' the fuselage, which was done. Although this delayed the programme, it gave the Taon a further speed advantage. On 25 July 1957, Bernard Witt made the first test flight of the first of three planned prototypes. The Taon met all the performance requirements, but had come along just a little late – the G.91 was chosen as NATO's tactical fighter, but only three countries bought it. The second prototype Taon (the Br.1002) was modified, and twice broke the 1000km (216-mile) closed-circuit speed record with speeds of 1046.65 and 1075km/h (650.36 and 667.98mph).

SPECIFICATIONS

CREW:	one
POWERPLANT:	one 21.58kN (4850lb-thrust) Bristol Orpheus B-Or-3 turbojet engine
MAX SPEED:	1180km/h (733mph)
MAX ALTITUDE:	unknown
SPAN:	6.80m (22ft 4in)
LENGTH:	11.24m (36ft 10in)
HEIGHT:	3.75m (12.30m)
WEIGHT:	loaded 5800kg (12,787lb)

The Taon was probably the best of the many designs offered to meet NATO's needs for a common ground-attack fighter. Delays in development and politics saw it fail to progress past the prototype stage. One Taon is preserved at France's Musée de l'Air.

Taon not only means 'horsefly', but is also an anagram of NATO and OTAN, the French acronym for the same organization.

An enlarged, twin-engined development of the Taon, the Breguet 1100, was offered for a separate French air force requirement. Although it was unsuccessful here, it was developed in conjunction with BAC to become the SEPECAT Jaguar.

Four 0.50in (12.7mm) Browning machine guns were mounted beneath the Taon's small intakes. Other proposed weapons included up to four 227kg (500lb) bombs, Nord 5103 missiles or SNEB rocket pods.

BRISTOL 138 (1936)

The 1930s were a time of record-breaking flights in terms of speed, distance, endurance and altitude. The latter required new technology to support aircrew in the upper atmosphere, where the air was thinnest. To recapture the world altitude record, the RAF commissioned Bristol to build two prototypes of a specialized high-altitude aeroplane in 1934. The Bristol 138 was an unremarkable design, optimized for lightness and powered by a Pegasus engine with a two-stage supercharger. The pilot was to wear a special pressure suit and helmet. Making its first flight on 11 May 1936, Squadron Leader F.R.D. Swain later achieved an altitude of 15,230m (49,967ft) on 28 September. An Italian pilot took the record in May 1937, but on 3 June Flight Lieutenant M.J. Adam recaptured it with a flight reaching 16,440m (53,937ft).

SPECIFICATIONS

CREW:	1
POWERPLANT:	One 373 kW (500 hp) Bristol Pegasus PE.VIS radial engine
MAX SPEED:	285km/h (177mph)
MAX ALTITUDE:	18,459m (54,000ft)
SPAN:	20.12m (66ft)
LENGTH:	13.41m (44ft)
HEIGHT:	3.12m (10ft 3in)
WEIGHT:	loaded 2,409kg (5,310lb)

The Bristol 138 was essentially a conventional and conservative design of mainly wooden construction with a fixed landing gear. The plane's technological advances were found mainly in the pilot's pressure suit and oxygen system.

Pilots of the Bristols wore a special pressurized suit with an 'oxygen helmet' akin to a diver's outfit. The flights of the 138 helped to advance the science of high-altitude flight.

The Type 138 was first flown with a standard Pegasus engine and a three-bladed propeller. After the oxygen system was perfected, it was refitted with a supercharged version with a four-bladed propeller for the record flights.

The second aircraft was designated the Bristol 138B and was going to be fitted with a supercharged Rolls-Royce Kestrel inline engine, although this conversion never took place.

DE HAVILLAND DH.108 SWALLOW (1946)

First flown on 15 May 1946 by Geoffrey de Havilland junior, the tailless DH.108 was intended as a testbed for the Comet airliner, but evolved into a high-speed research machine. The second of three prototypes broke up in flight over the Thames estuary in 1946, while practising for the 100km (62-mile) closed-circuit speed record attempt, killing Geoffrey de Havilland junior. The third prototype was lost in February 1950, but not before it had become the first British (and first turbojet) aircraft to officially exceed Mach 1.0. This machine had a more pointed nose than its predecessors and a larger Goblin 4 engine and took the 100km record with an average speed of 974.02km/h (605.23mph) on 12 April 1948. The first prototype was lost in May 1950, leaving none of these important machines for posterity.

SPECIFICATIONS
(2nd aircraft TG306)

CREW:	one
POWERPLANT:	one 14.68kN (3300lb-thrust) de Havilland Goblin 3 turbojet engine
MAX SPEED:	Mach 1.0
MAX ALTITUDE:	12,190m (40,000ft)
SPAN:	11.89m (39ft)
LENGTH:	7.47m (24ft 6in)
HEIGHT:	unknown
WEIGHT:	loaded 4064kg (8960lb)

John Derry flew the third DH.108 through the sound barrier in September 1948. Pitch control at transonic speeds was a constant problem, and all three DH.108s were lost in fatal crashes.

The third DH.108, VW120, had a revised canopy profile and more streamlined nose compared to its predecessors. It was lost due to a failure of the pilot's oxygen supply.

The second aircraft had a sweep of 45 degrees at the leading edge. The first had 43 degrees sweep. Control came from elevons used in conjunction with the rudder.

The fuselage was essentially that of the DH.100 Vampire, made mainly of wood. The first DH.108, in particular, made considerable use of Vampire components.

DOUGLAS D-558-I SKYSTREAK *(1947)*

After World War II, the US Navy conducted its own high-speed aeronautical research in a parallel but more modest programme to the US Air Force's X-Plane series. The first of the navy's experimental jets, designed by Edward 'Ed' Heinemann, received the designation D-558-I (or Phase One), which hardly rolled off the tongue. The name Skystreak helped a little, but the programme is less well known than its USAF counterparts, which took most of the glory. The first of three Skystreaks was first flown at Muroc Dry Lake, California, on 15 April 1947. Unlike the slightly faster X-1, the Skystreak was turbojet-powered and took off and landed under its own steam. As such, the records it set were more representative of the performance achievable by practical combat aircraft. Test pilot Howard Lilly was killed in NACA 141 when his engine compressor exploded at low level and cut the control cables.

SPECIFICATIONS

CREW:	one
POWERPLANT:	one 22.4kN (5000lb thrust) J35-A-11 turbojet engine
MAX SPEED:	1048km/h (651mph)
SPAN:	7.62m (25ft)
LENGTH:	10.88m (35ft 8.5in)
HEIGHT:	3.70m (12ft 2in)
WEIGHT:	maximum 4854kg (10,105lb)

The D-558-II first flew on 4 February 1984 and five years later became the first Mach 2.0 aircraft. Marine Major Marion Carl flew the Skyrocket to an unofficial record altitude of 25,370m (82,235ft).

There was no ejection seat at the time that could safely propel the pilot over the tail, so a jettisonnable nose capsule was designed instead.

Like the X-1, the D-558-I had a straight wing and a pivoting tailplane to provide pitch authority at speeds where the elevator would be ineffective.

The Skystreaks were originally painted the same high-visibility orange as the original X-1. Even the wheels were orange. This proved hard to see against a dark sky background, and the aircraft were repainted white.

The tailplane was mounted high up to avoid shockwave effects from the wing. The tailplane was a thinner section so as to prevent its own shock wave interfering with the wing's.

DOUGLAS D-558-II SKYROCKET (1948)

The Skyrocket represented the second phase of the US Navy's programme conducted with NACA to explore transonic flight and collect data for use in future combat aircraft design. The D-558 'Phase Two' went well beyond that, achieving Mach 2. It was a much more sophisticated aircraft than the D-558-I Skystreak, the Skyrocket having a swept wing and mixed jet and rocket propulsion. The Skyrocket was also normally air launched from a B-50 bomber rather than flown off the ground. The D-558-II pilots studied flight stability at transonic and supersonic speeds. Many of their findings contradicted the wind tunnel data, advancing the state of aerodynamic knowledge. It was intended to have a third phase, building an aircraft embodying the best features of the D-558-I and D-558-II; however, this project was cancelled. The three Skyrockets became display pieces.

SPECIFICATIONS (NACA 145)

CREW:	one
POWERPLANT:	one 26.69kN (6000lb-thrust) Reaction Motors LR-8-M-65 rocket and one 13.35kN (3000lb-thrust) Westinghouse J34-WE-40 turbojet engine
MAX SPEED:	2078km/h (1291mph)
MAX ALTITUDE:	25,370m (82,235ft)
SPAN:	7.62m (25ft)
LENGTH:	13.79m (45ft 3in)
HEIGHT:	3.86m (12ft 8in)
LAUNCH WEIGHT:	6925kg (15,266lb)

The D-558s were designed to explore the transonic regime between Mach 0.8 and 1.2, where there was little wind tunnel data. Although the Skystreak was built for structural strength rather than outright speed, it did set two records, the second at 1047km/h (650.796mph).

The first two Skyrockets initially flew with jet engines, later replaced by a rocket. The third aircraft had both a jet and a rocket. The rocket fuel was liquid oxygen and diluted ethyl alcohol.

In 1953 Scott Crossfield became the first man to reach twice the speed of sound when he flew NACA 144 to Mach 2.005, or 2078km/h (1291mph), in a dive on 20 November 1953.

Seven different wing configurations were trialled, including slats, fences, chord extensions and other devices. This contributed to ways of avoiding and recovering from pitch-up in transonic flight.

FAIREY DELTA 2 (1954)

To further the study of delta wing aircraft, Fairey was commissioned to build two true high-speed afterburning research machines. Two aircraft were built, with the RAF serials WG774 and WG777. The first was flown by Royal Navy pilot Peter Twiss on 6 August 1954. An engine failure and partial gear-up landing damaged WG774 and delayed the programme for eight months. The second aircraft was refitted with an RA.28R Avon and an 'eyelid' afterburner, which worked in a 'bang-bang' (on-off) manner. On 10 March 1956 the FD.2 took the world absolute speed record when Peter Twiss flew WG774 to 1822km/h (1132mph). This beat the record previously set by an F-100C Super Sabre by 500km/h (310mph) and was to last 21 months, a long time in those days of fast-paced aeronautical progress. WG774 was converted into the BAC.221 in conjunction with the Concorde project. WG777 is on display at the Royal Air Force Museum at Cosford, Shropshire.

SPECIFICATIONS (WG777)

CREW:	one
POWERPLANT:	one 58.27kN (13,100lb-thrust) Rolls-Royce RA.28R Avon afterburning turbojet engine
MAX SPEED:	1822km/h (1132mph)
MAX ALTITUDE:	unknown
SPAN:	8.18m (26ft 10in)
LENGTH:	15.74m (51ft 8in)
HEIGHT:	3.35m (11ft 0in)
WEIGHT:	loaded 6298kg (13,884lb)

The Delta 2 was the first aircraft to exceed 1600km/h (1000mph) and, despite official indifference, captured the world absolute speed record. The two aircraft went on to contribute to the design of Concorde.

Fuel capacity was very limited. With use of the aircraft's afterburner there was only about enough for 25 minutes flight at altitude.

Soon after the record-breaking flight the first FD.2 was painted an overall mauve colour with a cream cheatline. The second aircraft later became overall blue.

The FD.2s featured a 'droop snoot' nose for better forward visibility on take-off and landing. The nose was linked to the nosegear doors, which opened when the nose drooped.

FAIREY LONG-RANGE MONOPLANE (1928)

In 1928 the British Air Ministry commissioned two large aircraft specifically for an attempt on the long-distance straight-line distance record. The first of two Long-Range Monoplanes flew on 14 November 1928. In April 1929 Squadron Leader A.G. Jones-Williams and Flight Lieutenant N.H. Jenkins flew from Cranwell to Karachi (then in India) nonstop – a distance of 6647km (4130 miles), but were 219km (136 miles) short of the absolute record, set by Italians between Rome and Brazil. An attempt to fly nonstop from Cranwell, Lincolnshire, to Cape Town, South Africa, in December 1929 led to the loss of one Monoplane and crew in a crash at Tunis. In February 1933 Squadron Leader Oswald Gayford and Flight Lieutenant G.E. Nicholetts flew a Monoplane 8594km (5340 miles) from Cranwell to Walvis Bay (then in South Africa, today Namibia) in a flight lasting 57.5 hours.

SPECIFICATIONS

CREW:	two
POWERPLANT:	one 390kW (450hp) Napier Lion XIA/NS inline piston engine
MAX SPEED:	unknown
MAX ALTITUDE:	unknown
SPAN:	25.0m (82ft 0in)
LENGTH:	14.1m (48ft 6in)
HEIGHT:	3.1m (12ft 0in)
WEIGHT:	unknown

For a two-crew, single-engine aircraft, the Long-Range Monoplane set some remarkable distance records in the 1920s and 1930s, including the first aircraft to fly nonstop from England to India, a flight which took more than 50 hours.

The fabric-covered wing contained fuel tanks with a total capacity of 455 litres (1000 imperial gallons).

The Monoplane was a pure cantilever monoplane designed to have as little drag as possible. The clean fuselage lines led to the nickname 'Eversharp', after a maker of pens and pencils.

The Long-Range Monoplane had fixed undercarriage and a fixed-pitch propeller. The Napier Lion engine was essentially standard, but had higher compression pistons and specially tuned carburettors.

K1991

FFA P-16 (1955)

Swiss state aircraft manufacturer Flug-und Fahrzeugwerke A.G. (FFA) received a contract for a jet to replace various piston-engined ground-attack types in 1952. The P-16 was designed specifically for Swiss conditions, with particular emphasis on being able to operate from short alpine runways. The first prototype, the P-16.04, made its initial flight on 28 April 1955. It later crashed into Lake Constance following failure of one small component. Four pre-series aircraft were ordered and later so, too, were 100 production fighters. The third prototype also crashed in Lake Constance. The government used this as an excuse to cancel its orders, but FFA flew two more P-16s under civil registrations in 1959 and 1960. These armed aircraft were more representative of a production fighter and met all the Swiss Air Force's requirements, but did not lead to any new orders. The fifth and last P-16 is preserved at the Swiss Air Force Museum at Dubendorf.

SPECIFICATIONS

CREW:	one
POWERPLANT:	one 35.14kN (7900lb-thrust) Armstrong Siddeley Sapphire A.S.Sa.6 turbojet
MAX SPEED:	998km/h (620mph)
MAX ALTITUDE:	15,240m (50,000ft)
SPAN:	11.14m (36ft 7in)
LENGTH:	14.30m 46ft 11in)
HEIGHT:	4.25m (13ft 11in)
WEIGHT:	11,720kg (25,838lb)

Although the P-16 never entered service, the innovative wing design fed directly to Bill Lear's Learjet 23, and its influence can still be seen today in the large numbers of Learjets of various models on the civil registers of the world.

The thin wing did not allow any room for fuel, so the wingtip fuel tanks became a necessity. These are also a prominent feature of the Learjet family.

The P-16 had a particularly strong landing gear with dual wheels for rough field operation. The P-16 could operate from an airstrip only 494m (1620ft) in length.

The P-16's unswept, thin-section, high-aspect ratio wing was designed both for high subsonic cruise speeds and low landing speeds, qualities that also proved suitable for small business jets.

J-3001

LEDUC RAMJETS *(1947)*

Ramjet enthusiast René Leduc began work on his 010 test aircraft in 1937, development of which was halted by World War II. On 19 November 1946 the 010 began its test programme with a series of captive flights aboard a modified SE.161 Languedoc transport. Delays in receiving vital equipment held up free flights until 21 October 1947, when Jean Gonord flew the aircraft clear of the Languedoc on the 010's first gliding flight. The first flight under ramjet power was delayed until 21 April 1949, 12 years after design work began. A second similar aircraft, the 016, began captive trials in 1951 and flew under turbojet power in January 1952. The next model was the 021, which made its first powered flight on 7 August 1953 and recorded a climb rate of 12,000m (39,370ft) per minute and a ceiling of 19,995m (65,600ft). The 022 was slightly larger than the 021, with swept wings, and was capable of climbing to 24,994m (82,000ft) in four minutes.

SPECIFICATIONS

CREW:	one
POWERPLANT:	one 19.61kN (4409lb-thrust) Leduc thermo propulsive ramjet
MAX SPEED:	680km/h (423mph)
MAX ALTITUDE:	17,000m (55,777ft)
SPAN:	10.52m (34ft 6in)
LENGTH:	10.25m (33ft 6in)
HEIGHT:	unknown
WEIGHT:	loaded 2800kg (6173lb)

The Leduc 010 was the first aircraft to fly with ramjet power alone. In all, there were five Leduc ramjet aircraft: one 010, one 016, two 021s and one 022. The 016 and 022 are preserved at France's Musée de l'Air.

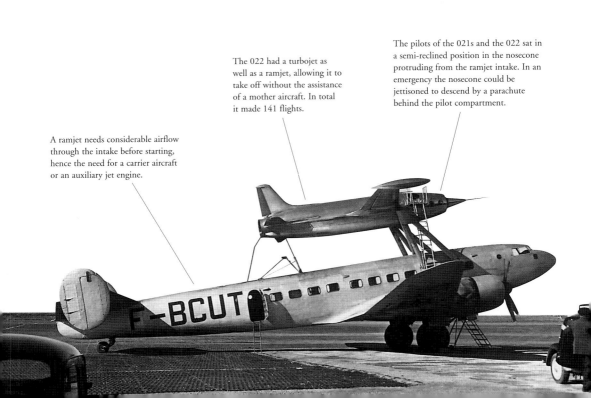

A ramjet needs considerable airflow through the intake before starting, hence the need for a carrier aircraft or an auxiliary jet engine.

The 022 had a turbojet as well as a ramjet, allowing it to take off without the assistance of a mother aircraft. In total it made 141 flights.

The pilots of the 021s and the 022 sat in a semi-reclined position in the nosecone protruding from the ramjet intake. In an emergency the nosecone could be jettisoned to descend by a parachute behind the pilot compartment.

LOCKHEED A-12 BLACKBIRD (1962)

The A-12 was the single-seat progenitor of the Blackbird family and stemmed from a 1958 CIA request for a Mach 3-plus reconnaissance aircraft to replace the U-2, which even before Gary Powers's 1960 shootdown was considered too vulnerable for overflying the USSR. Designed under great secrecy and with the codename Archangel by 'Kelly' Johnson at the Lockheed 'Skunk Works', the first prototype was flown on 25 April 1962 by Lockheed test pilot Lou Schalk. During 1963–64 the A-12s reached various milestones, including flight at Mach 3 and cruise at Mach 3.2 at 25,298m (83,000ft). Unfortunately by then a treaty had banned overflights and the A-12's reconnaissance equipment was unsuitable for oblique photography. The A-12s did fly some missions over North Vietnam and North Korea in 1967–68, but the programme was terminated in 1968 in favour of the more sophisticated two-seat SR-71 with its dedicated reconnaissance systems operator.

SPECIFICATIONS

CREW:	one
POWERPLANT:	two 144.57kN (32,500lb-thrust) Pratt & Whitney J58 afterburning turbojet engines
MAX SPEED:	(cruise) 3661km/h (2269mph)
MAX ALTITUDE:	25,908m (84,978ft)
SPAN:	16.9m (55ft 7in)
LENGTH:	31.0m (102ft 0in)
HEIGHT:	5.5m (18ft 3in)
WEIGHT:	maximum 54,421kg (120,000lb)

The A-12 offered higher resolution photography and a faster top speed than the SR-71, but its equipment was rendered partly obsolete by treaty, and its mission was more than a handful for one crewman.

The first A-12 flights were made with two J75 engines because the J58 was not ready. In October 1962 an A-12 flew with one J75 and one J58, and by early 1963 had two J58s, allowing it to achieve its design speed of Mach 3.2.

Four of the ten A-12 airframes were lost in testing or service, including two at the secret Groom Lake base in Nevada. The six remaining examples are preserved in museums around the USA.

Unlike the SR-71, the A-12 was designed to directly overfly the target, rather than stand off outside enemy sensors and image it with long-range sensors, including cameras and radar.

LOCKHEED AH-56 CHEYENNE (1967)

ased largely on the research work done with the XH-51, Lockheed won the contract to build the US Army's AAFSS (Advanced Aerial Fire Support System) with its AH-56 Cheyenne. On 21 September 1967 Don Segner made the first flights of the AH-56. Its unique propulsion system allowed the Cheyenne to reach more than 400km/h (250mph), a remarkable speed for any rotorcraft.

One of the 10 Cheyenne prototypes was lost in a flying accident, while another was destroyed in the wind tunnel. The US Air Force disliked its army counterparts having a helicopter that performed like a fighter-bomber and (partly as a consequence) the army decided it wanted something smaller and lighter. The whole programme was cancelled completely in 1972, and eventually the US Army got the AH-64 Apache, developed by Boeing.

SPECIFICATIONS

CREW:	two
POWERPLANT:	one 2563kW (3435hp) General Electric T64-GE-16 turboshaft engine
MAX SPEED:	408km/h (254mph)
MAX ALTITUDE:	7925m (26,000ft)
ROTOR DIAMETER:	15.36m
LENGTH:	18.30m (60ft 0in)
HEIGHT:	4.10m (13ft 6in)
WEIGHT:	maximum 13,600kg (29,983lb)

The Cheyenne had similar capabilities to a World War II medium bomber, with the added ability to hover and fly backwards. It had its teething troubles, but the main reason for its cancellation was US Air Force jealousy.

The armament consisted of two turrets, one with a 30mm (1.18in) cannon and the other with a grenade launcher or a Gatling-type machine gun. Anti-tank missiles and rockets could be carried on the stub wings.

The AH-56 had a rigid main rotor, which did not tilt to give forward thrust as in a conventional helicopter; an anti-torque tail rotor; and a pusher propeller at the tail. This gave the propulsive force.

By adjusting the blade pitch, the pusher propeller was found to be very effective as an airbrake. This permitted 'dive-bombing' manoeuvres, although bombs were never actually carried.

LOCKHEED XH-51A (1962)

In 1959 a rigid rotor test helicopter was built under the Lockheed designation CL-475 and was followed by two prototypes of the CL-495, built with a gyroscope ring system for stabilization. Rigid rotors rotate only in cyclic pitch and are thus stiffer than hinged or teetering rotors, and the gyro-stabilizer controls the pitch of the rotor disc.

The CL-495s received the US Army designation XH-51A and first flew in 1962 under a joint US Army/US Navy programme. In May 1965 one XH-51A was changed to 'compound' configuration, with a J60 jet engine bolted to the port side and 5.18m (17ft) stub wings attached. The Lockheed XH-51A Compound could handle up to 3g even at speed, and had a steeper maximum bank angle and faster hover turn rate than found on conventional helicopters. Flown by US Army pilot Major Emil Kluever, it set an unofficial record speed of 486.9km/h (302.6mph) in 1965.

SPECIFICATIONS (XH-51A)

CREW:	one
POWERPLANT:	one 410kW (550hp) PT-6B-9 turboshaft and one 12.9-kN (2900lb-thrust) Pratt & Whitney J60-P-2 jet engine
MAX SPEED:	487km/h (303mph)
MAX ALTITUDE:	3048m (10,000ft)
ROTOR DIAMETER:	10.67m (35ft 0in)
FUSELAGE LENGTH:	9.75m (32ft 0in)
HEIGHT:	2.74m (9ft 0in)
WEIGHT:	loaded 2041kg (4500lb)

Many of the features found on the XH-51A high-speed rigid-rotor compound helicopter were incorporated into the AH-56 Cheyenne attack helicopter. This failed to enter service, despite its merits, and was to be the last Lockheed helicopter.

Both the XH-51As are preserved at the Army Aviation Museum at Fort Rucker, Alabama, although both are believed to be in storage.

The gyro system consisted of a 1.37m (4ft 6in) diameter ring mounted between the rotors and the fuselage top, and linked by arms to each of the rotor blades (three blades on the XH-51; four on the XH-51 Compound).

One hope for the CL-495 design was that it would lead to a craft that could take off like a helicopter, then fold its rotors away for flight like a conventional aeroplane.

A pod was carried on the starboard wing of the XH-51 Compound, probably to balance the weight of the J60 jet engine mounted on the port side.

LOCKHEED NF-104 STARFIGHTER (1963)

Under the name Aero Space Trainer (AST), three Lockheed F-104As were modified to give experience of extreme high-altitude flight and weightlessness to astronauts and those in the X-15 programme. The first of these was delivered to NASA in October 1963.

To boost the already exceptional performance of the F-104, a Rocketdyne rocket motor was fitted in the tail. This would work in thin air where the jet was barely functional. At extreme altitudes aerodynamic controls were also ineffective, and reaction control jets in the nose, tail and wingtips were needed to provide control as the NF-104 approached the edge of the atmosphere.

Chuck Yeager was forced to eject from an NF-104 in December 1963 while attempting a zoom climb to more than 30,480m (100,000ft). Another NF-104 suffered rocket explosions in 1965 and 1971, and was not repaired after the latter incident. The survivor is mounted outside the Air Force Flight Test Center HQ at Edwards Air Force Base in California.

SPECIFICATIONS

CREW:	one
POWERPLANT:	one 65.84kN (14,800lb-thrust) General Electric J79-GE-3A/3B afterburning turbojet engine and one 26.69kN (6000lb-thrust) Rocketdyne LR-1212/AR2 rocket engine
MAX SPEED:	2130 km/h (1,324mph)
MAX ALTITUDE:	36,820m (120,800ft)
SPAN:	7.25m (23ft 9in)
LENGTH:	16.66m (54ft 8in) + rocket
HEIGHT:	4.11m (13ft 5in)
WEIGHT:	loaded 9979kg (22,000lb)

A few modifications to the basic F-104A fighter allowed it to reach double its normal combat ceiling. The NF-104 was one of the most spectacular and cost-effective NASA rocket programmes, although had its fair share of accidents and incidents.

Modifications to the F-104A included a larger F-104G-style rudder and extended wingtips. A longer ventral fin was fitted during the course of the programme.

The throttleable rocket engine was able to be controlled within a range of 14.35 to 28.7kN (3000 to 6000lb-thrust). The rocket burn time was about 105 seconds.

The extended wingtips gave more lift at high altitude and housed the reaction control puffer jets for roll control.

In December 1963, Major R.W. Smith reached an altitude of 36,820m (120,800ft) in an NF-104. This was a record for aircraft taking off from the ground under their own power.

MESSERSCHMITT ME 263 *(1944)*

T he Me 263 was the result of an attempt to remedy the faults of the Me 163 Komet, including its extremely limited endurance and its skid landing system, which often wrecked the aircraft. Begun as a derivative of the Komet-designated Me 163D, the aircraft was also designed by Alexander Lippisch, but handed to Junkers to refine and build as the Ju 248. It returned to a Messerschmitt designation as the Me 263 by the time it flew in August 1944. Larger than the Me 163, with fuel tanks in the wings and a conventional undercarriage, the 263 had a 'cruise chamber' in the engine, which allowed it to return to altitude between attacks on bomber formations. Carefully used, this stretched the endurance to one hour. It is thought that two Me 263s were built, but that only one flew in Germany (as a glider). After the end of World War II, a captured example was flight tested in the USSR.

SPECIFICATIONS

CREW:	one
POWERPLANT:	one 16.68kN (3750lb-thrust) Walter HWK 109-509C-4 rocket motor
MAX SPEED:	estimated 1000km/h (620mph)
MAX ALTITUDE:	unknown
SPAN:	9.50m (31ft 2in)
LENGTH:	7.88m (25ft 11in)
HEIGHT:	2.70m (8ft 10in)
WEIGHT:	5150kg (11,354lb)

Production difficulties and the war's end prevented any powered flights by the Me 263 in German hands. It was a more practical approach to a rocket fighter than the Me 163, however, and was carefully studied in the USSR.

The Me 263 was built in three sections. The cabin and nosewheel were in the front; the fuel tanks, cannon and main wheel wells were in the centre section; and the rear section was detached for access to the Walter rocket motor.

A cut-down rear fuselage and a bubble canopy improved the rearwards view compared to that of the Me 163. Unlike the Komet, the 263 had a pressurized cockpit.

The engine had an additional 'cruise chamber' giving 2.9kN (660lb-thrust), and this had its own exhaust below the main rocket. The motor was longer than the airframe builders expected, and the fuselage had to be lengthened slightly.

VD+ER

MYASISCHEV VM-T ATLANT (1981)

Fulfilling a similar role to NASA's modified 747 Shuttle Carrier Aircraft, the Atlant was a Myasischev 3M 'Bison' bomber modified to carry huge external loads such as rocket launcher components from the manufacturer to the Baikonur launch site. With weights up to 40 tonnes (88,183lb) and diameters of 8m (26ft), such loads could not be carried aboard any existing aircraft. Three Bisons were rebuilt under the designation VMT Atlant, with new tails and external mounting points. One was a static test example, but the first flying VMT took to the air on 29 April 1981. The engines were upgraded during the Atlant's career, and the aircraft provided sterling service in support of the Energia rocket and space shuttle Buran programmes. They were eventually replaced by the Antonov An-225, which could carry large internal loads as well as items piggyback style.

SPECIFICATIONS

CREW:	five
POWERPLANT:	four 421.6kN (94,800lb-thrust) RKBM/Koliesov VD-7MD turbojets
MAX SPEED:	500km/h (310mph)
MAX ALTITUDE:	cruising altitude 8500m (27,887ft)
SPAN:	53.6m (174ft 5in)
LENGTH:	52.2m (167ft 11in)
HEIGHT:	10.6m (34ft 9in)
WEIGHT:	maximum 192,000kg (423,208lb)

The Atlant was able to carry components of the huge Energia rocket, external fuel tanks or the Buran space shuttle. One example is preserved at the Russian Air Force Museum at Monino.

The bomber's standard single fin and tailplanes were replaced by a new extended rear section. This had a dihedralled tailplane with two huge endplate fins. These were mounted outside the disturbed airflow of most payloads.

Fourteen different mounting points were fitted to the VMT's fuselage to accommodate the supports for different types of external load. The Buran shuttle, for example, required seven of the mounting points.

The first of the two flying VM-Ts was equipped with a refuelling probe in the nose. Carriage of a large external load increased drag and fuel consumption, and reduced the aircraft's maximum speed.

NORTH AMERICAN X-15 (1959)

The most extraordinary of the X-planes, the X-15 was designed to explore extreme high-speed flight up to and beyond the edge of the atmosphere. The first of three X-15 airframes flew on 8 June 1959, piloted by Scott Crossfield, who had contributed to the aircraft design. The first 25 fights were made with a pair of XLR-11 rockets before the big XLR-99 was available. A 1960 ground test explosion delayed the programme slightly. A 1967 landing accident damaged the second aircraft, which was rebuilt as the longer, more capable X-15A-2. The third X-15 was lost in a fatal crash in November 1967.

On 3 October 1967 Pete Knight made the most extraordinary of all the X-15's flights, reaching Mach 6.72 (7297km/h or 4534mph) and an altitude of 107,960m (354,200ft) in the X-15A-2. This was the last X-15A-2 flight, but the programme carried on until October 1968 and the 199th flight of the series.

SPECIFICATIONS

CREW:	one
POWERPLANT:	one 253.55kN (57,000lb-thrust) Reaction Motors XLR-99 rocket engine
MAX SPEED:	6608km/h (4104mph)
MAX ALTITUDE:	95,931m (314,750ft)
SPAN:	6.81m (22ft 4in)
LENGTH:	15.32m (50ft 3in)
HEIGHT:	3.53m (11ft 7in)
WEIGHT:	loaded 14,183kg (31,275lb)

The X-15 programme expanded the manned aircraft flight envelope through Mach 4, 5 and 6, and to 108km (67 miles) above the earth's surface. Dropped by a B-52, the X-15s left and re-entered the atmosphere before gliding to land.

The X-15 pilots wore full pressure suits, which served as the prototypes for those used in the Mercury, Gemini and Apollo rocket programmes. For those X-15 flights that exceeded 100km (62 miles) altitude, the pilots won astronaut wings.

Later flights of the X-15A-2 used an ablative coating with a white outer layer. This burnt away during re-entry to show the pink inner core. Even then the airframe itself occasionally suffered damage from the intense heat.

The X-15 was mainly constructed of titanium and stainless steel with a coating of an exotic alloy called Inconel X, which could withstand temperatures up to 680°C (1200°F).

55

SCALED COMPOSITES PROTEUS (1998)

Another extraordinary design by Burt Rutan, the Proteus was created as a high-altitude multi-mission aircraft that would operate above 18,280m (60,000ft) with an endurance of over 14 hours. Proposed missions included reconnaissance, atmospheric research, commercial imaging, and space launch. One idea was to have fleets of a (possibly unmanned) version that would orbit over major cities acting as TV and communications relay platforms, although the company that claimed it required 100 aircraft did not in the end order any. The first flight took place on 23 July 1998, and since then the single Proteus has flown over the Pacific and North Pole on various missions and been displayed at the Paris Air Show. Recent missions include tests in UAV avoidance techniques and atmospheric measurements over the Azores.

SPECIFICATIONS

CREW:	two
POWERPLANT:	two 10.23kN (2300lb-thrust) Williams International FJ44-2E turbofans
MAX SPEED:	297km/h (187mph)
MAX ALTITUDE:	19,202m (63,000ft)
SPAN:	23.65m (77ft 7in)
LENGTH:	17.17m (56ft 4in)
HEIGHT:	5.36m (17ft 7in)
WEIGHT:	maximum 7031kg (15,500lb)

The Proteus high-altitude/long-operation (HALO) aircraft is suitable for various kinds of observation, communications and scientific research. So far only one has been built, but has performed research missions all over the world.

The modular construction of the Proteus allows for the replacement of mission payloads and engines, and varying the length of the wings as required by the particular mission.

The canard foreplanes are longer than the wings of many aircraft. The port canard has a servo tab on struts, to help activate this large structure at higher speeds.

The Proteus can be operated from the ground like a UAV, although all tests to date have used safety pilots. The usual accommodation is for a pilot and a mission specialist.

RUTAN VOYAGER (1984)

D esigned for one purpose – to make the first nonstop flight around the world without aerial refuelling – the Voyager is the largest aircraft designed to date by Burt Rutan and first flew on 22 June 1984. The crew for the record flight comprised Burt Rutan's brother Dick and Dick's girlfriend Jeana Yeager. Loaded with fuel, the Voyager scraped its wingtips on the ground when it took off from Mojave, California, on 14 December 1986. The wingtip extensions or winglets were damaged and had to be shaken loose before it continued. Flying a path that weaved·above and below the equator, it returned to nearby Edwards Air Force Base nine days later on 23 December. During its epic flight, Voyager flew an official distance of 42,212km (24,986 miles) at an average speed of 186km/h (116mph), in an elapsed time of 216 hours, 3 minutes and 44 seconds.

SPECIFICATIONS

CREW:	two
POWERPLANT:	one 82kW (110hp)
	Teledyne Continental
	IOL-200 piston engine
	and one 97kW (130hp)
	Teledyne Continental
	0-240 piston engine
MAX SPEED:	approx. 241km/h (150mph)
MAX ALTITUDE:	over 6248m (20,500ft)
SPAN:	33.8m (110ft 8in)
LENGTH:	8.9 m (29ft 2in)
HEIGHT:	3.1 m (10ft 3in)
WEIGHT:	empty 1020kg (2250 lb)

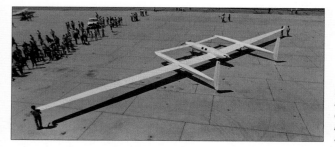

The remarkable Voyager became the first aircraft to fly nonstop unrefuelled around the world. After its nine-day circumnavigation it never flew again, being dismantled and donated to the Smithsonian Institution.

Voyager was constructed of 98 per cent composite materials, mainly a sandwich of paper honeycomb and graphite fibre, which was carefully moulded, then oven cured.

N269VA

The front engine was used for the first 70 hours of the flight when the Voyager was heaviest and to climb over bad weather. The rear engine ran for the whole nine days.

The winglets were mainly used as housings for the fuel vents, so that the fuel would not drain out on the ground. The aircraft contained 17 fuel tanks with a total of 3181 kg (7011lb) of fuel aboard at take-off.

SUKHOI T-4 *(1972)*

Sometimes said to be a Soviet copy of the North American XB-70, the Sukhoi T-4 (sometimes called Project 100, or Su-100) flew eight years later and was somewhat smaller. It was an extremely ambitious programme, intended to fly at Mach 3 and using materials new to Soviet industry; it was preceded by several Su-9 fighters modified as testbeds with different wing planforms or canard foreplanes. Vladimir Ilyushin and navigator Nikolaay Alfyorov made the T-4's first flight on 22 August 1972. It had been intended to have six prototypes, leading to a fleet of 250 operational bombers. As with the XB-70, the vast cost of the T-4 saw its cancellation. Only 10 test flights were made up to January 1974, with a total flight time of 10 hours and 10 minutes. Five flights were made with the landing gear down, and the maximums achieved, on the ninth flight, were a speed of Mach 1.28 and an altitude of 12,000m (39,370ft).

SPECIFICATIONS

CREW:	two
POWERPLANT:	four 156.91kN (35,273lb-thrust) Kolesov RD36-41 afterburning turbojet engines
MAX SPEED:	planned 3200km/h (1987mph)
MAX ALTITUDE:	planned 24,000m (78,740ft)
SPAN:	22.00m (72ft 2in)
LENGTH:	44.50m (146ft 0in)
HEIGHT:	11.19m (36ft 9in)
WEIGHT:	maximum 136,000kg (299,823lb)

With a proposed top speed of Mach 3 and a cruise speed of Mach 2.8, the Sukhoi T-4 would have been the highest-performing Soviet aircraft. Even the Soviet leadership blanched at the cost and put the money into the Tu-22M 'Backfire' instead.

The T-4's nose was drooped at 12 degrees for ground movement and low-speed flight, presenting a pilot's windscreen that would not have been out of place on a tramcar. When the nose was raised, the pilot had no forward view at all, and had to operate entirely on instruments.

The T-4 had what was possibly the first fly-by-wire control system. This was used on every flight except one, where a test of the mechanical back-up was tried. This functioned satisfactorily, but required a lot of attention and effort by the pilot to maintain control.

The T-4 made extensive use of titanium and stainless steel throughout its structure. To cope with the extreme temperatures expected at Mach 3, the nosecone was made of a special ceramic material.

WRIGHT 1903 FLYER *(1903)*

Dayton, Ohio, bicycle makers Wilbur and Orville Wright began a scientifically based programme to achieve powered flight in 1899, progressing through a series of manned and unmanned gliders to work out the problems of stability and control. The powered Flyer was finished in July 1903 and later dismantled for transport to Kitty Hawk, North Carolina, where both reliable winds and privacy could be had. On 17 December 1903, Orville Wright made the first successful powered flight, travelling for just 37m (120ft) in a flight lasting 12 seconds. Three more flights were made with the Flyer that day, the longest being 260m (852ft) in distance. Just after its fourth flight, a gust of wind caught the Flyer and turned it over. It was badly damaged and never flew again.

SPECIFICATIONS

CREW:	one
POWERPLANT:	one 89.5kW (12hp) water-cooled piston engine
MAX SPEED:	50km/h (30mph)
MAX ALTITUDE:	unknown
SPAN:	12.3m (40ft 4in)
LENGTH:	6.4m (21ft)
HEIGHT:	2.8m (9ft 3in)
WEIGHT:	with pilot 339kg (750lb)

The 1903 Flyer is the great-grandfather of all 'X-planes', being the culmination of years of research, model building and wind tunnel testing, culminating in a successful (if short) flight test programme.

The structure of the Flyer was spruce and ash covered in muslin cloth. The four-cylinder engine wa the Wrights' own design. It weighed 81kg (179lb), nearly one-third of the aircraft's empty weight.

The 1903 Flyer was displayed for many years at London's Science Museum due to a dispute between the Wrights and the Smithsonian, but now has pride of place in the National Air and Space Museum in Washington DC.

The Flyer's pilot lay prone on a cradle on the lower wing, using a handle to operate the canard elevator and shifting his hips to pull wires which warped the wings and moved the rudder.

POWERPLANT PERMUTATIONS

Until 1939, all aircraft had flown under the power of a piston engine. The first experimental jet aircraft offered little performance improvement over propeller-driven aircraft, but the piston engine was nearing the zenith of its development by 1945 and jets soon became dominant.

Rocket motors seemed to offer interceptors the key to reaching the high altitudes of the new jet bombers. Rockets improved over the years from simple one-shot devices to sophisticated powerplants with fully variable throttles, but remained incredibly fuel thirsty. By the time they reached altitude rocket interceptors had little time to engage the enemy before they had to fly (or glide) back to base. Mixed-powerplant designs (rocket and jet) were a short-lived compromise.

Combining the gas turbine with the propeller to create the turboprop proved a huge success, but not in combat aircraft. Early turboprops were large, gave less power than expected and emitted unbearable noises. Only a small number of turboprop ground attack aircraft entered service, but the design evolved to find its niche in transports, patrol aircraft and trainers.

Left: *An experimental interceptor with incredible performance, the YF-107A lost out to the F-105 Thunderchief.*

AVRO ASHTON *(1950)*

The Avro 688 Tudor was a largely unsuccessful post-war British airliner, built in a number of versions, but only a handful of each of them. The second prototype Tudor I was converted as a jet research aircraft with four Nene 5 engines. Redesignated the Tudor 8, it flew as a jet on September 6 1948, beating the Comet 1 by nearly a year. The Tudor 8 was intended as a pure research aircraft, however and not as a commercial transport. The Tudor 8 was followed into the air on 1 September 1950 by the first Type 689 Tudor 9, later known as the Ashton. This differed in having Nene 6 engines, a new tail unit with a square fin tip and a tricycle undercarriage. As well as exploring the general questions of jet operation and navigation, at least one Ashton was used in tests of bombing equipment.

SPECIFICATIONS

CREW:	five
POWERPLANT:	four 22.24kN (5,000lb-thrust) Rolls-Royce Nene 6 turbojet engines
MAX SPEED:	707km/h (439mph)
MAX ALTITUDE:	12,344m (40,500ft)
SPAN:	36.58m (120ft 0in)
LENGTH:	(27.31m 89ft 7in)
HEIGHT:	9.53m (31ft 3in)
WEIGHT:	loaded 37,195kg (82,000lb)

Like the Avro Canada Jetliner, the Ashton was based around the basic design of the Tudor. In fact the five Ashtons were built using surplus Avro Tudor 2 fuselages as a quick way to get a fleet of jet research aircraft.

The flight crew consisted of a pilot and co-pilot, a navigator, flight engineer and radio operator. Extra crew could be carried for observing different test tasks.

Six Ashtons were ordered but only five were built. Ashton 1 WB490, Ashton 2s WB491 and 492, Ashton 3 WB493 and Ashton 4 WB494. The fuselage of WB491 is preserved at the Newark Air Museum.

The four engines were coupled in two nacelles. This reduced the asymmetric effect of a single engine failure.

AVRO CANADA C.102 JETLINER (1949)

The 50-passenger Jetliner missed being the world's first jet airliner to fly by just 13 days when it took to the air on 10 August 1949. The crew were Jimmy Orrel, Don Rogers and Bill Baker. Six days later, on its second flight, it suffered a belly landing but was quickly repaired. The C.102 achieved over 800km/h (500mph) and 12131m (39,800ft) during over 500 hours of testing,

The Korean War interfered in several ways, and there were no orders. Howard Hughes wanted Convair to build Jetliners under licence, but the US government wouldn't allow him to use factory space for a civil aircraft. Avro Canada chose to concentrate on its CF-100 fighters. The prototype was cut up in 1956 and only the nose was saved for preservation.

SPECIFICATIONS

CREW:	3 or 4 and 36 passengers
POWERPLANT:	four 16.01kN (3,600lb-thrust) Rolls-Royce Derwent 5 turbojet engines
MAX SPEED:	737km/h (458mph)
MAX ALTITUDE:	12131m (39,800ft)
SPAN:	29.90m (98ft 1in)
LENGTH:	25.12m (82ft 5in)
HEIGHT:	8.06m (26ft 5in)
WEIGHT:	maximum 29,484kg (65,000lb)

Canada lost a potential lead in the post-war aviation scene when its Jetliner was cancelled. It was not until such aircraft as the Boeing 727 appeared in the mid-1960s that small jets for domestic routes were made available.

The Jetliner shared a number of features with the UK Avro Company's Tudor piston engined airliner, mainly the fuselage and wing shape.

The Royal Canadian Air Force became the first air arm with jet transports, but these were de Havilland Comets. Trans Canada Airlines bought the Vickers Viscount turboprop in 1955.

The Jetliner was the first jet transport to fly into the USA and was extensively tested in warm conditions as well as cold temperatures. It was designed to operate in a temperature range from -28 to +50°C (-20 to +120°F).

BELL XP-83 *(1945)*

To meet a USAAF requirement for a long range jet fighter, Bell chose the same general configuration for the XP-83 as used on their P-59, but enlarged to have more room for fuel and armament. On 25 February 1945 Jack Wooliams made the first flight of XP-83 44-84990. The second aircraft did not fly until October, after the end of the war. The XP-83 proved somewhat disappointing, being unstable and underpowered. The engine outlets were too close to the tailplanes and caused them to buckle from heat during ground run-ups. In general the XP-83 offered no significant improvement over Lockheed's P-80, and further development as a fighter was abandoned. The two aircraft did have a role in testing ramjets but in September 1946 one ramjet engine caught fire, causing a crash. The remaining aircraft was scrapped the following year.

SPECIFICATIONS

CREW:	one or two
POWERPLANT:	two 17.79kN (4,000lb-thrust) General Electric J33-GE-5 turbojet engines
MAX SPEED:	840km/h (522mph)
MAX ALTITUDE:	13,715m (45,000ft)
SPAN:	16.15m (53ft 0in)
LENGTH:	13.66m (44ft 10in)
HEIGHT:	4.65m (15ft 3in)
WEIGHT:	maximum 10,927kg (24,090lb)

The portly XP-83 was not a suitable basis for a combat aircraft when there were better designs in the pipeline. It remains one of the lesser-known US fighter aircraft.

The problem of the jet efflux damaging the tailplane was cured by changing the angle of the exhausts. Extending the tail was proposed to fix the instability but never carried out.

As with the XP-59, the second XP-83 prototype was later fitted with a rudimentary second seat for a flight test engineer. When one aircraft crashed, both crew were lucky to escape.

The fuselage was wider mainly to accommodate extra fuel tanks. The two engines were attached under the wing roots and did not really impinge on the fuselage space.

BEREZNYAK-ISAYEV BI *(1941)*

Almost as soon as Aleksandr Bereznyak and Aleksei Isayev proposed a rocket-powered interceptor on 9 July 1941, a team was put to work on creating the BI, which made its first flight as a glider on 10 September 1941. The factory had to be evacuated and relocated to the east to escape the German advance. This delayed the first rocket-powered flight until 15 May 1942, and the BI-1 damaged its undercarriage on landing. Despite the lack of test data, 50 BIs were already being built by the time the third prototype crashed on the type's seventh flight. Captain Grigory Bakhchivandzhi, who had made the first flight was killed in March 1943 when the BI-3 pitched down during a high-speed run. The BI programme slipped in priority and became purely experimental. The BI-6 was tested with wingtip ramjets in an attempt to extend the feeble endurance, but these were not a success.

SPECIFICATIONS

CREW:	one
POWERPLANT:	one 10.78kN (2,425lb-thrust) Dushkin/Shtokolov D-1A-1100 rocket motor
MAX SPEED:	estimated 900km/h (559mph)
MAX ALTITUDE:	unknown
SPAN:	6.60m (21ft 8in)
LENGTH:	6.94m (21ft 9in)
HEIGHT:	unknown
WEIGHT:	maximum 1,683kg (3,710lb)

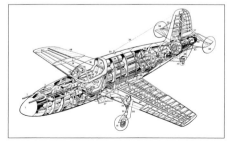

Conceived in the confusion following the German invasion, the BI was the first aircraft powered by a liquid-fuelled rocket. Despite this lead over the Luftwaffe, only seven aircraft were completed.

The fuel was a volatile mix of red fuming nitric acid and kerosene. At full power, the 705kg (1,554lb) of fuel was consumed in two minutes.

The airframe was of all-wood construction. The fuselage was plywood with a fabric coating. The flaps, fuel tanks and parts of the engine compartment had substantial metal components.

The BIs had a retractable ski undercarriage for winter use, which included a small skid on the ventral fin. The aircraft's first powered take-off was made from skis.

CONSOLIDATED VULTEE XP-81 (1945)

To meet a USAAF requirement for a long range fighter to escort B-29 bombers to Japan, Consolidated Vultee chose a mixed powerplant XT-40 turboprop and J33 jet arrangement for their XP-81. First flown from the dry lake at Muroc, California on February 11, 1945, the XP-81 was initially fitted with a Packard Merlin piston engine from a P-51 Mustang, due to teething problems with the XT-40. The first flight using the XT-40 took place on 21 December 1945, making the XP-81 the world's second turboprop aircraft after the Trent Meteor. Unfortunately the XT-40 (also known as the TG-33) never gave the expected power, and performance was no better than the Merlin version. The capture of island bases closer to Japan and the end of the war saw the military requirement for the XP-81 vanish. The turboprop technology showed promise and the two aircraft continued flying until 1947.

SPECIFICATIONS

CREW:	one
POWERPLANT:	one 1,716kW (2,300hp) General Electric XT31-GE-1 turboprop and one 16.68kN (3,750lb-thrust) Allison J33-GE-5 turbojet engine
MAX SPEED:	816km/h (507mph)
MAX ALTITUDE:	10,820m (35,500ft)
SPAN:	15.39m (50ft 6in)
LENGTH:	13.69m (44ft 10in)
HEIGHT:	4.27m (14ft 0in)
WEIGHT:	loaded 8,845kg (19,500lb)

The XP-81 was one of the many promising aircraft that remained at the prototype stage because of the war's end. The final use of the two prototypes was as photography targets on a bombing range. Their remains are being combined into a display example.

To give the longest range, the operational technique would have been to use the turboprop alone for cruising flight with the jet being used only on take-off and for bursts of high speed.

Armament of a production P-81 would have been six machine-guns or cannon and up to 1451kg (3,200lb) of bombs.

Poor directional stability on the first flights led to the fitting of a small ventral fin and a 38cm (15in) extension to the fin. The second aircraft had a rounded fin tip and a larger ventral fin.

CONVAIR YB-60 *(1952)*

To compete for the USAF's strategic jet bomber requirement, Convair proposed modifying their B-36, which had straight wings and was powered by six piston engines, and in some versions, four podded jets as well, in an all-jet swept-wing design. Based on the B-36F, the new aircraft was to be the B-36G but was renamed the B-60 before completion. On 18 April, 1952 Beryl Erickson made the first flight of the YB-60. Three days before, Boeing's competitor, the all-new YB-52 Stratofortress flew. In comparison with the B-52, the Convair had a much larger wing, but its gross weight and useful load was lower. It had a lower stalling speed, but a cruising speed 87km/h (54mph) slower. Even then the control surfaces had been designed for the slower B-36 and the forces needed for manoeuvering were much higher. The YB-60 began a flight test programme, but only 44 hours were flown before the USAF cancelled any further plans for it in August 1952. The second YB-60 was never completed. Both aircraft were put aside at Fort Worth and eventually scrapped.

SPECIFICATIONS

CREW:	five
POWERPLANT:	four 38.70kN (8,700lb-thrust) Pratt & Whitney J57-P-3 turbojet engines
MAX SPEED:	818km/h (508mph)
MAX ALTITUDE:	16,242m (53,300ft)
SPAN:	62.79m (206ft 0in)
LENGTH:	52.12m (171ft 0in)
HEIGHT:	18.44m (60ft 6in)
WEIGHT:	maximum 185,973kg (410,000lb)

A modified B-36 was Convair's approach to the USAF's strategic bomber needs. It proved that starting from scratch, as Boeing did with the B-52 was the way to go, and the YB-60 lasted only a short time when its comparative deficiencies were realised.

Increased speed was the main defence of the YB-60. Instead of the multiple gun turrets of the B-36, only the twin 20-mm cannon in the tail remained.

The YB-60's crew was concentrated in the pressurized forward compartment. There were only five crew members, pilot, co-pilot, navigator, bombardier/radio operator and radio operator/tail gunner, rather than the 13-man crew of a standard B-36.

DASSAULT SUPER MIRAGE 4000 (1979)

Originally called the Super Mirage Delta, the Super Mirage 4000 was built as a private venture by Dassault in the hope of taking a lead in the market for advanced multi-role warplanes.

On 9 March 1979, flown by Jean-Marie Saget, the Mirage 4000 made its initial flight, reaching Mach 1.2 in the process. The 4000 made much use of advanced composite construction materials and a sophisticated fly-by-wire controls system, using canard foreplanes to counter its inherent instability caused by an aft centre of gravity. Its complexity and expense was too much for export customers and the French military were looking to the next generation – eventually procuring Dassault's own Rafale. The Super Mirage 4000 played a role in developing the latter's control system and engines before retirement in 1987 to the Musée de l'Air at Le Bourget.

SPECIFICATIONS

CREW:	one
POWERPLANT:	two 83.36kN (18,740lb-thrust) SNECMA M53-2 afterburning turbojet engines
MAX SPEED:	2,445 km/h (1,520mph) (Mach 2.3)
MAX ALTITUDE:	20,000m (65,615ft)
SPAN:	12.00m (39ft 4in)
LENGTH:	18.70m (61ft 5in)
HEIGHT:	5.80m (19ft 0in)
WEIGHT:	loaded 16,100kg (35,494lb)

The Super Mirage 4000 was a scaled-up twin-engined Mirage 2000 with canard foreplanes. It flew soon after the Mirage 2000, but there was no official requirement for it and no export orders.

The fly-by-wire active control system allowed for the centre of gravity to be well aft. The natural instability allowed the nose to be pointed quickly at any target.

The 4000 had three times as much internal fuel as the Mirage 2000. Even the vertical fin contained a fuel tank and the maximum combat radius was over 2000km (1,243 miles).

Large parts of the airframe were non-metallic, including the fin, rudder, elevons, fuselage access panels and canard foreplanes, which were carbon fibre.

F-16 MATV/VISTA *(1993)*

Originally a combined project between General Electric, General Dynamics and the Israeli Defence Force, who wanted an even more manoeuvrable F-16, the F-16 MATV (Multi Axis Thrust Vectoring) programme became a US-only affair in 1992. Using a borrowed USAF F-16D Block 30 (86-0048), the aircraft flew as the F-16 VISTA (Variable Stability Inflight Test Aircraft) in its new form on 2 July 1993. The main feature was the Axisymmetric Vectoring Exhaust Nozzle (AVEN). Pratt & Whitney ended its plan to series produce a TVC F110 in 1997 and the F-16 VISTA was given a standard engine and nozzle. In 2000 the F-16 VISTA was in use again, this time on JSF helmet-mounted-display trials. It has also been used to develop flight control software for the F/A-22 and the Indian Light Combat Aircraft (LCA).

SPECIFICATIONS

CREW:	two
POWERPLANT:	one 122.77kN (27,600lb-thrust) General Electric F110-GE-100 afterburning thrust-vectoring turbojet engine
MAX SPEED:	2,125km/h (1,320mph)
MAX ALTITUDE:	over 15,240m (50,000ft)
SPAN:	9.45m (31ft 0in)
LENGTH:	L15.0m (49ft 3in)
HEIGHT:	5.01m (16ft 8in)
WEIGHT:	maximum 8,981kg (19,800lb)

The F-16 VISTA aircraft had a more sophisticated thrust vectoring system than the F-15 STMD and enabled manoeuvres at extreme angles of attack. The concept next appeared in some versions of the Sukhoi 'Flanker' family.

The failure of the thrust vectoring system could potentially lead to a deep stall and spin. A large spin-recovery parachute was mounted on a rig at the tail.

As a counterbalance to the AVEN nozzle and the anti-spin parachute, an extra 318kg (700lb) of balance was added to hardpoints on the engine intake.

The exhaust nozzle could be deflected in any direction through an angle of up to 20 degrees. This allowed sustained flight at up to 86 degrees angle of attack, and transient flight at 180 degrees (i.e. backwards).

GLOSTER E.28/39 *(1941)*

In September 1939, to test Frank Whittle's new jet engine in flight, the British Air Ministry commissioned an aircraft from the Gloster company. Sometimes called the Gloster Whittle, Gloster Pioneer or the G.40, the resulting machine was formally designated the E.28/39 (the 28th prototype ordered in 1939). On 15 May 1941 at Cranwell, Lincolnshire, Gerry Sayer made the first flight of a British jet aircraft, taking W4041/G on a short flight. Various improved versions of Whittle's Power Jet engines were tested, and a second prototype joined the programme in March 1943. Unfortunately it crashed after an aileron failure in July, but the pilot bailed out. The first prototype continued flight tests until 1944, by which time the much-improved Meteor was entering service. It has been in the collection of the Science Museum, London, since 1946.

SPECIFICATIONS
(as first flown)

CREW:	one
POWERPLANT:	one 3.82kN (869lb-thrust) Power Jets W1 turbojet engine
MAX SPEED:	544km/h (328mph)
MAX ALTITUDE:	9755m (32,000ft)
SPAN:	8.84m (29ft 0in)
LENGTH:	7.72m (25ft 4in)
HEIGHT:	2.70m (8ft 10in)
WEIGHT:	loaded 1700kg (3748lb)

The E.28/39 was the first jet aircraft to fly outside Germany. It was a structurally and aerodynamically simple aircraft, intended only to act as a testbed for Whittle's jet engine, pictured here.

Problems were encountered with engine oil and lubricants freezing at high altitude. The second prototype crashed when the wrong grease was used on the ailerons and one stuck in position, sending the aircraft out of control.

The E.28/39 was first fitted with a W1X engine with only 2.76kN (620lb-thrust) for ground tests. The W1 of 3.82kN (869lb-thrust), the W1A of 5.16kN (1160lb-thrust) and the W2/500 of 7.56kN (1700lb-thrust) followed.

Late in the test programme small auxiliary fins were fitted to the tailplane to provide additional stability at high speeds. The E.28/39 was not very fast but had a good climb rate and ceiling.

GLOSTER TRENT METEOR (1945)

The Gloster Meteor was flown with a wide variety of jet engines, including the Welland, Derwent, Beryl, Avon, Nene and Atar. The wing-mounted engine layout allowed the fitting of various powerplants for test purposes. Engine testbed is a common use for a high-performance multi-engined aircraft, with one engine replaced by a test example, but Meteor F.1 EE227 went one step further by replacing both and becoming the world's first turboprop aircraft to fly, on 20 September 1945, the pilot being Eric Greenwood. The Trent turboprops were modified Derwent jets driving 2.4m (7ft 11in) diameter five-bladed propellers. The engines generated both horsepower and thrust, and the Trent Meteor proved nearly as fast as the standard F.1 fighter. Its test career contributed greatly to solving the problems of turboprop engine and propeller control.

SPECIFICATIONS

CREW:	one
POWERPLANT:	two 560kW (750hp) Rolls-Royce RB.50 Trent turboprop engines
MAX SPEED:	756km/h (470mph)
MAX ALTITUDE:	unknown
SPAN:	13.10m (43ft 0in)
LENGTH:	12.57m (41ft 3in)
HEIGHT:	3.96m (13ft 0in)
WEIGHT:	standard F.1 6257kg (13,795lb)

EE227 was a Meteor F.1 which had seen active service with No. 616 squadron. Modified with turboprops, it contributed to the long list of firsts achieved by the Meteor.

EE227 had five-bladed fully feathering Rotol propellers. Their diameter was restricted by the low-slung nacelles, and five blades were needed to give sufficient pull.

The tail of EE227 was modified several times during its career. Small vertical fins were added to the tailplane for extra lateral stability, particularly when flying with one prop feathered.

The Trent Meteor had a longer stroke undercarriage to give more clearance between the propeller blades and the ground.

HEINKEL HE 178 *(1939)*

Like Whittle in England, Hans-Joachim Pabst von Ohain was working on a jet engine for years before World War II. Heinkel built a simple high-winged aircraft as a testbed for von Ohain's engine. On 24 August 1939 Erich Warsitz flew the He 178 V1 for the first time. On the second flight a few days later, the intake sucked in a bird and the engine lost thrust; however, a safe landing was made. A few more flights were carried out and a demonstration for the German Air Ministry (Reichsluftfahrtministerium, or RLM) was held in November, but attracted little interest. Heinkel moved on to the twin-engined He 280. A second (V2) prototype with a longer wingspan was built, but was apparently never flown. The He 178 V1 was put on display at the Berlin Air Museum, but was destroyed during World War II in an Allied bombing raid in 1944.

SPECIFICATIONS

CREW:	one
POWERPLANT:	one 4.41kN (992lb-thrust) Heinkel He S 3B turbojet
MAX SPEED:	640km/h (398mph)
MAX ALTITUDE:	n/a
SPAN:	7.20m (23ft 7in)
LENGTH:	7.48m (24ft 6in)
HEIGHT:	2.10m (6ft 9in)
WEIGHT:	loaded 1950kg (4,300lb)

The He 178 was the first jet to fly, but it faced official indifference. The chance to develop a 'war winning' fighter was squandered. Little documentation and few photographs remain of its test programme.

The He 178's fuselage was made of dural metal, but the wings were of wooden construction, with an elliptical planform that was something of a trademark of Heinkel aircraft.

The Heinkel turbojet only gave 4.41kN (992lb-thrust) when first flown in the He 178, but was modified to provide 4.90kN (1102lb-thrust) during testing. This was partly brought about by a shift from gasoline to diesel fuel.

Despite its tiny engine, the He 178 had a better performance than contemporary piston-engined fighters. The conservatism of the Air Ministry at the time led Heinkel and von Ohain to continue jet development as a private venture.

HEINKEL HE 280 *(1941)*

The Heinkel He 280 was developed in 1939 as a practical successor to the He 178. Following trials in 1940 of the He 280 V1 as a glider, on 2 April 1941 the V2 made its first flight powered by two Heinkel-Hirth HeS 8 turbojets. When the development of this engine was stopped, Jumo 004 and BMW 003 engines were tested in subsequent prototypes, of which there were a total of eight. One He 280 was flown in mock combat with a Focke-Wulf Fw 190 and easily defeated it, but the Air Ministry was for some reason not impressed and jet development was halted. When it was urgently restarted, Ernst Heinkel had fallen further out of political favour, and the more advanced but lower performing Me 262 was selected for further development.

SPECIFICATIONS

CREW:	one
POWERPLANT:	two 8.24kN (1852lb thrust) Junkers Jumo 004A turbojets
MAX SPEED:	817km/h (508mph)
MAX ALTITUDE:	unknown
SPAN:	12.0m (39ft 4in)
LENGTH:	10.20m (33ft 5in)
HEIGHT:	3.19m (10ft 5in)
WEIGHT:	loaded 3350kg (7386lb)

The He 280 was the first twin-engined jet and the first jet aircraft designed as a warplane. Designed as a fighter rather than an interceptor, it was more manoeuvrable than the Me 262 and could have been in service earlier had politics not intervened.

The He 280 first flew with no engine cowlings because pooled fuel had caught fire in the cowls during ground tests and it was thought safer to leave them off.

The He 280 was the first aircraft ever fitted with an ejection seat. On 13 January 1942 a Heinkel test pilot became the first pilot to use one in an emergency when the controls of his He 280 froze up.

The structural soundness of the twin tail arrangement was not trusted by the Air Ministry, and this was another count in favour of Messerschmitt's fighter.

Unlike the first Me 262 prototypes, the He 280s had a tricycle undercarriage, which allowed a level take-off and landing.

JUNKERS JU 322 MAMMUT (1941)

To deliver troops in an invasion of Britain, the German Air Ministry (RLM) commissioned Junkers to build an enormous flying wing glider called the Ju 322 Mammut ('Mammoth'), capable of carrying up to 140 troops, a truck or a light tank. Two hundred examples were ordered. The Ju 322 had a conventional tail and a nose door for loading vehicles. In early ground tests the floor proved too weak to hold a tank and had to be strengthened. The extra weight of the reinforcement reduced the payload considerably. The Ju 322 is believed to have made only one flight, in April 1941. The take-off trolley was destroyed, and the Mammut proved very unstable in pitch and had to be cut free from the Ju 290 tow plane to avoid disaster. The Mammut landed in a rough field, where it remained for two weeks until it could be retrieved. By then the RLM had given up on the Ju 322 and the invasion of Britain had been postponed for ever. The Messerschmitt Me 321 glider, which later proved adaptable to piston-engine power as the Me 323, was selected as the Luftwaffe's strategic transport; the two finished and 98 partially completed Mammuts were cut up and used as firewood. Only one photograph of the Mammut is known to exist (see opposite).

SPECIFICATIONS

CREW:	two
POWERPLANT:	none
MAX SPEED:	n/a
MAX ALTITUDE:	n/a
SPAN:	62m (203ft 5in)
LENGTH:	30.25m (99ft 3in)
HEIGHT:	10m (32ft 9in)
WEIGHT:	loaded 36,000kg (79,366lb)

Junkers was a pioneer in metal construction, so it was surprising it was asked to build one of the world's largest wooden aircraft in 1941, having not made a wooden aircraft since 1928.

The cockpit was mounted on the starboard side of the centre section's top surface to make the least obstruction in the freight hold.

A nose loading door was a rare feature for a wartime aircraft. One of the few others to have this arrangement was the Messerschmitt Gigant, which also began as a glider.

KYUSHU J7W1 SHINDEN *(1945)*

The J7W1 Shinden (Magnificent Lightning) was probably the most radical piston-engined fighter put into production in World War II. Of canard pusher configuration, it was designed to outperform all existing Japanese and Allied types. Three wooden MXY6 gliders with canards were tested from late 1943, and one of these received a small piston engine. With the basic concept proven, the Kyushu firm was given the contract to develop a full-size fighter in June 1944. The first of two Shinden prototypes was finished in April 1945, by which time the type had already been put into production. Engine cooling problems, parts shortages and the dire war situation delayed the first flight until 3 August 1945. On that day the Shinden's designer Captain Masaoki Tsuruno took the Shinden aloft three times. The war ended a week later, and the Shinden never flew again.

SPECIFICATIONS

CREW:	one
POWERPLANT:	one 1492kW (2000hp) Mitsubishi Ha 43-42 radial piston engine
MAX SPEED:	estimated 750km/h (466 mph)
MAX ALTITUDE:	estimated 11,887m (39,000ft)
SPAN:	11.1m (36ft 6in)
LENGTH:	9.7m (31ft 8in)
HEIGHT:	3.9m (12ft 10in)
WEIGHT:	maximum 5228kg (11,526lb)

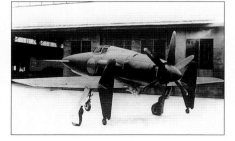

Built by Kyushu mainly because it had the capacity, the extraordinary Shinden flew only three times, always with the gear down. Its designer had envisaged a jet design, but in the end it became an exhibit at the National Air and Space Museum.

During its extremely brief test career the Shinden was found to suffer from strong vibrations at full power, mainly from the propeller and drive shaft. It also had a tendency to pull to the right.

The Shinden was armed with four 30mm (1.18in) Type 5 cannon with 450 rounds. This heavy (in every sense) armament was mounted in the nose and balanced the engine in the rear.

The pusher configuration dictated a tricycle undercarriage layout so as to keep the six-bladed propeller clear of the ground. The three mainwheels and the two auxiliary wheels could be retracted, but never were.

LOCKHEED X-26B/QT-2 (1967)

From 1968 five Schweizer SGS 2-32 gliders were used by the US Navy's Test Pilot School under the designation X-26A. The US Army took two further 2-32s and had Lockheed modify them under a secret programme as the QT-2 (the initials standing for 'Quiet Thruster'), later redesignated X-26B. The first QT-2 first flew on 11 August 1967, piloted by Quintin Burden. It differed in having a mid-mounted four-cylinder piston engine, which drove a large two-bladed propeller through a long extension shaft over the cockpit. The army's aim was to develop an observation and reconnaissance platform for use over Vietnam that had a long endurance and a low acoustic signature. After secret tests in the USA, the two QT-2s were tested in Vietnam under combat conditions in 1968. Although little is known about their achievements, they led to the follow-on Q-Star and YO-3A four-seat observation aircraft.

SPECIFICATIONS
(Lockheed X-26B)

CREW:	two
POWERPLANT:	one 76kW (100hp) Continental O-200 A piston engine
MAX SPEED:	185km/h (115mph)
MAX ALTITUDE:	3962m (13,000ft)
SPAN:	17.4m (57ft 2in)
LENGTH:	9.39m (30ft 9in)
HEIGHT:	2.82m (9ft 3in)
WEIGHT:	loaded 990kg (2182lb)

The X-26B was a modified sailplane, optimized for long, quiet patrols over Southeast Asia, laden with sensors for seeking enemy movements in the jungle. As such it was the slowest and lightest of all the X-Planes.

The standard SGS 2-32 glider was of metal construction with fabric-covered control surfaces. As the QT-2, a large fibreglass engine cover, tail fairing and propeller spinner were added.

The propeller was mounted at the end of a long aluminium shaft. Different blade configurations were trialled from three to six blades, all operating at low rpm for low acoustic signature.

N5713S

EXPERIMENTAL

The undercarriage consisted of a single large mainwheel, a small tailwheel and a nosewheel which prevented the nose scraping the ground on take-off or landing.

MACCREADY GOSSAMER ALBATROSS (1979)

Following the successful Gossamer Condor, which won the first Kramer Prize for human-powered flight by completing a set figure-of-eight course in 1977, engineer and designer Paul MacCready built the Gossamer Albatross to attempt the first human-powered crossing between England and France. The Albatross was built for absolute lightness, with a foam and carbon-fibre structure covered in thin transparent film. On 12 June 1979, piloted by professional cyclist Bryan Allen, the Albatross flew across the English Channel, a distance of 35.8km (22.25 miles) in 2 hours and 49 minutes, and won the second Kramer prize. The backup aircraft, the Albatross II, was tested by NASA at Edwards Air Force Base with pilot power, electric power and as a towed glider. The results contributed to other large, lightweight aircraft such as the Pathfinder and Helios.

SPECIFICATIONS
(*on Channel flight)

CREW:	one
POWERPLANT:	one human
MAX SPEED:	29km/h (18mph)*
MAX ALTITUDE:	15m (49ft 2in)*
SPAN:	29.77m (97ft 8in)
LENGTH:	10.36m (34ft 0in)
HEIGHT:	4.88m (16ft 0in)
WEIGHT:	loaded 100kg (221lb)*

The Albatross was the most successful HPA (human-powered aircraft) and was a triumph of weight reduction and maximizing the power output of one man pedalling furiously.

The ribs and leading edges of the wings were made of polystyrene foam and covered by a skin of transparent Mylar film. The empty weight of the Albatross was only 32kg (71lb), less than that of the pilot.

The Albatross is in the Smithsonian's National Air and Space Museum collection, while the Albatross II is displayed at the Museum of Flight in Seattle, Washington.

Like the Wright Flyer, the Albatross was of canard configuration with a pusher propeller. As the Wright brothers did, Paul MacCready perfected the configuration by building many flying models beforehand.

The Albatross was powered by the pilot pedalling continuously. The pedals, cranks, drive chain, seatpost and a few fittings and wires were the only metal parts.

MARTIN XB-51 *(1949)*

Begun as the XA-45 under a 1945 USAAF jet attack bomber requirement, Martin's contender underwent numerous changes before it flew for the first time on 28 October 1949 as the XB-51. With the outbreak of war in Korea, the new US Air Force (USAF) changed its requirement to that of night intruder. In a competitive fly-off, the English Electric Canberra with its longer range and greater loitering time proved superior, and the XB-51 was cancelled in November 1951. The USAF ordered 250 Canberras as the B-57, then gave Martin the licence to build them. After the official cancellation the two XB-51s kept flying on test work on such things as high-speed bomb release and collected useful data on bicycle landing gear. One made an appearance as the fictional 'Gilbert XF-120' fighter in the film *Toward the Unknown*. Both were lost in fatal crashes, one in 1952 and the other in 1956.

SPECIFICATIONS

CREW:	two
POWERPLANT:	three 27kN (6000lb-thrust) General Electric J47-GE-13 turbojet engines
MAX SPEED:	1038km/h (645mph)
MAX ALTITUDE:	12,344m (40,500ft)
SPAN:	16.17m (53ft 1in)
LENGTH:	25.92m (85ft 1in)
HEIGHT:	5.27m (17ft 4in)
WEIGHT:	maximum 28,330kg (62,457lb)

One of the only three-engined jet combat aircraft, the XB-51 had several innovative features and good performance, although its strength was questionable. The rotating bomb bay design was adapted for use when Martin license-built the Canberra as the B-57.

The crew consisted of a pilot seated under the bubble canopy and a navigator seated in the fuselage behind and below the pilot's cockpit.

The rotating internal weapons bay could carry up to four 726kg (1600lb) bombs. Two 907kg (2000lb) bombs could be carried externally.

Mounting the engines on the forward fuselage and in the tail allowed for an exceptionally clean wing.

NORD 1500 GRIFFON *(1955)*

The 1500.01 Griffon I was intended to further explore ramjet propulsion beyond Mach 2. Powered originally by an Atar 101G-2 turbojet, then by an Atar 101F, it accomplished its first flight in September 1955. It was then modified to become the 1500.02 Griffon 2 with the addition of a Nord ramjet and a much larger air intake, and first flew as such in 1957 piloted by André Turcat, who later made the first Concorde flight.

The two engine systems were co-axial and could be run simultaneously, giving a very impressive performance. A series of time-to-height records were set, and in October 1960 the Griffon II reached Mach 2.19. In February 1959 Turcat had broken the 100km (62-mile) closed-circuit speed record at 1643km/h (1020mph). Proposals for a production Super Griffon were overtaken by developments in conventional afterburner-equipped engines.

SPECIFICATIONS

CREW:	one
POWERPLANT:	one Atar 101F turbojet engine and one Nord ramjet engine
MAX SPEED:	Mach 2.19
MAX ALTITUDE:	17,983m (59,000ft)
SPAN:	15.72m (51ft 7in)
LENGTH:	8.12 (26ft 7in)
HEIGHT:	4.69m (15ft 5in)
WEIGHT:	loaded 7250kg (15,983lb)

The Griffon's configuration was ahead of its time, with an underslung intake and canard foreplanes. The fuel-thirsty ramjet gave high speed but low endurance, and development was halted. The Griffon was retired to display at the Musée de l'Air.

The Griffon II's top speed was limited more by heating considerations than by engine limits. The proposed Griffon III would have been of all-steel construction to withstand the temperatures from friction heating at higher Mach numbers.

Initially the Griffon flew with a heavily framed canopy, but this was replaced by a clear unit late in its flying career.

The ramjet and turbojet were mounted co-axially on the Griffon II, allowing both to operate independently or together. The turbojet was needed to get the aircraft to a speed where the ramjet could be started.

NORTH AMERICAN YF-107A (1956)

Initially intended to be a fighter-bomber version of the F-100 with a semi-recessed weapons bay, the YF-107 emerged as a high-performance dual-role interceptor, with a secondary attack capability. North American test pilot J.R. 'Bob' Baker exceeded Mach 1 on the YF-107A's maiden flight on 10 September 1956. Less than two months later it reached Mach 2. The top speed achieved was Mach 2.3. A sophisticated flight control system allowed the F-107 to roll at supersonic speed. The F-107 lost out to the F-105 Thunderchief to become the US Air Force's main tactical fighter-bomber in 1957, but served on for several more years with NASA on research duties. One of the three YF-107s was wrecked in a landing accident with NASA, but the other two are preserved, at Pima, Arizona, and Dayton, Ohio.

SPECIFICATIONS

CREW:	one
POWERPLANT:	one 104.5kN (23,500lb-thrust) Pratt & Whitney J75-P-9 afterburning turbojet engine
MAX SPEED:	2480km/h (1541mph)
MAX ALTITUDE:	14,630m (48,000ft)
SPAN:	11.15m (36ft 7in)
LENGTH:	18.56m (60ft 10in)
HEIGHT:	6.00m (19ft 8in)
WEIGHT:	max 18,841kg (41,537lb)

The YF-107 began under the designation F-100B, but changed so much in the design phase that it was renamed before completion. The YF-107 had impressive performance and was sometimes called the 'Ultra Sabre' or 'Ultra Hog'.

The intake had a variable-area inlet duct system that regulated the airflow to the engines at speeds up to Mach 2. An unusual feature was the replacement of the rudder by an all-moving vertical fin.

Only the last of the three F-107s was equipped with armament, having four M39 20mm (0.79in) cannon as found on the standard Super Sabre.

A semi-recessed pod under the fuselage was designed to carry a nuclear weapon.

NORTHROP TACIT BLUE (1982)

'Tacit Blue' was a US Defense Department code name for a 'black' (secret) testbed aircraft designed to survey a wide area of battlefield and relay radar information to ground commanders. First flown in February 1982 by Dick Thomas, the Tacit Blue was flown 135 times by at least five different pilots over a three-year period. Its main role was to test if a Hughes multi-mode-side-looking radar (SLAR) could be carried in a stealth aircraft without giving away its position. The Tacit Blue also carried ELINT (electronic intelligence) antennas for intercepting enemy communications. It proved capable of operating safely close to the front line without detection, but the decision was taken to put the Hughes radar in a more conventional platform, and this became the E-8 J-STARS.

All the testing was done in complete secrecy. The Tacit Blue never received a USAF designation or serial, and has no known manufacturer's model number.

SPECIFICATIONS

CREW:	one
POWERPLANT:	two 24.6kN (5540lb thrust) Garrett ATF3-6 high-bypass turbofan engines
MAX SPEED:	cruise 462km/h (287mph)
MAX ALTITUDE:	operating altitude 9140m (30,000ft)
SPAN:	14.81m (48ft 7in)
LENGTH:	17.03m (55ft 10in)
HEIGHT:	3.23m (10ft 7in)
WEIGHT:	13,608kg (30,000lb)

Sometimes known as 'The Whale' or 'Shamu', the Tacit Blue was kept a secret from all but a few for 15 years. It was publicly revealed in April 1996 shortly before its donation to the USAF Museum.

The Tacit Blue had a quadruple-redundant digital fly-by-wire flight system that stabilized the aircraft about the longitudinal and directional axes.

The engine intake was recessed into the upper fuselage to shield it from ground-based radars, which easily pick up moving compressor faces.

Aspects of the Tacit Blue design and equipment found their way into the B-2 Spirit stealth bomber, also built by Northrop, and the E-8 J-STARS platform converted by Northrop from 707 airframes.

RFB FANTRAINER (1977)

In 1975 the West German defence ministry tasked RFB (Rhein-Flugzeugbau GmbH, a subsidiary of MBB) with building two prototypes of its Fantrainer. This was conceived as a military primary trainer that could give students the effects of jet aircraft handling with the running and maintenance costs of a turbine propeller aircraft. The prototype, which had two Wankel engines, first flew on 27 October 1977. These engines were soon replaced with an Allison 250 turboshaft (as used mainly in helicopters). This drove a Hoffmann five-blade constant-speed ducted fan mounted in the mid section of the fuselage.

Sometimes regarded as an unsuccessful concept, the Fantrainer was not bought by the Luftwaffe, but it was sold to Thailand. In 1982 the Thais signed a deal to buy and assemble 47 aircraft – 31 Fantrainer 400s designated as the B.F.18, and 16 B.F.18A Fantrainer 600s.

SPECIFICATIONS
(Fantrainer 400A)

CREW:	two
POWERPLANT:	one 313kW (420hp) Allison 250-XC20B turboshaft engine
MAX SPEED:	370km/h (200mph)
MAX ALTITUDE:	6100m (20,000ft)
SPAN:	9.70m (31ft 10in)
LENGTH:	9.48m (31ft 1in)
HEIGHT:	3.00m (9ft 10in)
WEIGHT:	maximum 1600kg (3527lb)

Dismissed by some as something of a glorified model aeroplane, the Fantrainer was the first modern full-scale ducted fan aircraft. As well as the Thai aircraft, at least one of the prototypes is still airworthy in Germany.

106

The two crew used a Stencel Ranger escape system where rocket-launched parachutes pulled the pilots out of their seats in an emergency. Conventional ejection seats were available as an option.

The Fantrainer 600 had a higher powered (485kW/650hp) version of the Allison 250. The Fantrainer 400 and 600 had 92 per cent commonality. Both were extremely quiet.

The Thai Fantrainers initially had glassfibre wings, but they were later rebuilt with all-metal wings constructed in Thailand.

ROCKWELL X-31 *(1990)*

The first US X-plane in several years, the X-31 was instituted under a US/German Enhanced Fighter Maneuverability (EFM) programme. Built by Rockwell International and MBB (DASA), the X-31's first flight was made by Rockwell pilot Ken Dyson on 11 October 1990. Using its vectored thrust engine it could fly beyond the normal aerodynamic stall and demonstrate previously 'impossible' manoeuvres. A very sophisticated digital fly-by-wire system with four flight control system computers kept the X-31 in the air despite its natural instability. Canard foreplanes and (later) aft fuselage strakes gave the necessary pitch control.

On 19 January 1995 the first aircraft was lost when it went out of control near Edwards Air Force Base; the pilot ejected. The programme ended that year, but the X-31 flew again in a US Navy programme that continued until 2003.

SPECIFICATIONS

CREW:	one
POWERPLANT:	one 71.2kN (16,000lb-thrust) General Electric F404-GE-400 afterburning turbofan
MAX SPEED:	Mach 1.28
MAX ALTITUDE:	unknown
SPAN:	7.28m (23ft 10in)
LENGTH:	without probe 13.20m (43ft 4in)
HEIGHT:	4.45m (14ft 7in)
WEIGHT:	loaded 7303kg (16,100lb)

Post-stall manoeuvering as demonstrated by the X-31 offered the potential for an unbeatable combat aircraft that could point its nose (and weapons) at will. The surviving X-31 is part of the Deutsches Museum collection in Munich, Germany.

Nearly half the X-31 was comprised of systems and components from other aircraft, including the V-22, F/A-18. F-5E, F-20, C-130, A-7, F-16XL and Cessna Citation.

The crash of the first X-31 was attributed to icing in the pitot tube, which prevented accurate information reaching the flight control system, causing the computers to put the aircraft in an unrecoverable position.

The X-31's thrust-vectoring system used three heat-resistant paddles which deflected into the exhaust flow in response to control stick and rudder movements.

SHORT SA.4 SPERRIN (1951)

Two prototypes of the Sperrin medium jet bomber were ordered as a hedge against the failure of the more sophisticated V-bombers (Victor, Vulcan and Valiant). On 10 August 1951 Tom Brooke-Smith made the first flight of SA.4 VX158. By then the V-bomber prototypes had proved acceptable for further development, and the two SA.4s were relegated to various research tasks, including as engine testbeds. In this role VX158 had a de Havilland Gyron mounted in first one, then the other lower nacelle. The name Sperrin (after a mountain range in Northern Ireland) was applied only towards the end of the programme, when only VX161 was in use for weapons trials, including that of the Blue Boar TV-guided bomb. It was retired in July 1956. Both Sperrins were subsequently scrapped.

SPECIFICATIONS (VX161)

CREW:	five
POWERPLANT:	four 28.91kN (6500lb-thrust) Rolls-Royce Avon RA-3 turbojet engines
MAX SPEED:	912km/h (567mph)
MAX ALTITUDE:	13,716m (45,000ft)
SPAN:	33.2m (109ft)
LENGTH:	31.14m (102ft 2in)
HEIGHT:	8.69m (28ft 6in)
WEIGHT:	maximum 52,163lb (115,000lb)

The Sperrin was of conservative aerodynamic design. By the time it had flown, swept wing bombers such as the Boeing B-47 were in service. The two aircraft were used for radar training, weapons and engine trials.

The pilot was the only crew member to have an ejection seat. The others had to escape through a floor chute in an emergency.

The 'under and over' engine layout was not a widely used configuration, but proved successful on the Lightning, which used afterburning versions of the Avon.

The bomb-aimer reached his position in the extreme nose by way of a pressurized tunnel from the cockpit. A radio operator and two navigators sat below and behind the pilot and co-pilot.

SUD-OUEST SO.6020 ESPADON (1948)

Sud-Ouest's 6020 Espadon (Swordfish) was France's first indigenous jet fighter design. The 6020-01 first flew on 12 November 1948. Its Nene engine had a ventral intake, which proved rather problematic. The third prototype (6020-03) had a longer ventral intake and also sported a SEPR 251 liquid-fuelled rocket under the fuselage. It was redesignated the SO.6025.

The SO.6021 was a lighter development with a larger wing and new fin. It had lateral intakes and was also tested with Turboméca Marboré wingtip jet engines. It was little improvement over the 6020 and suffered from heavy buffet at some speeds. With the same engine as the 6020 it was still underpowered. The rocket-boosted 6020-02 was the fastest of the series. Modified as the SO.6026 it achieved Mach 1.0 in level flight in 1953. By then better Dassault fighters were in production.

SPECIFICATIONS (SO.6021)

CREW:	one
POWERPLANT:	20.30kN (4564lb-thrust) Hispano-Suiza Nene turbojet engine
MAX SPEED:	Mach 0.96
MAX ALTITUDE:	12,000m (39,372ft)
SPAN:	10.60m (34ft 9.33in)
LENGTH:	15.0m (49ft 2.5in)
HEIGHT:	4.55m (15ft 5.75in)
WEIGHT:	loaded 6870kg (15,145lb)

The Espadon fighter was built in a complex series of prototypes under different designations. They were deemed unsuitable for further development, but did much to bring French industry into the jet age.

The SO.6021 was the first of the Espadons to have an ejector seat. It also had electrically powered controls, wingtip jets and six 20mm (0.79in) cannon.

The Espadons had only slightly swept wings. The more powerful swept-winged Dassault Mystère was flying by early 1951 and was much more promising, particularly in light of Korean War experience.

The SEPR liquid-fuelled rocket was a three-chamber unit that gave an additional 4.5kN (1012lb-thrust). It was also used on the Trident fighter.

SUD-OUEST TRIDENT (1953)

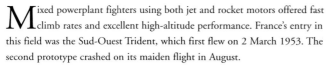

Mixed powerplant fighters using both jet and rocket motors offered fast climb rates and excellent high-altitude performance. France's entry in this field was the Sud-Ouest Trident, which first flew on 2 March 1953. The second prototype crashed on its maiden flight in August.

Despite its futuristic looks, the Trident had an unswept parallel-chord wing and a fuselage without area ruling (or wasp-waisting). The nose section served as an escape pod in an emergency.

The improved Trident II had large flaps, an ejection seat and a taller undercarriage. There were a number of accidents, including the unexplained inflight explosion of one aircraft. A missile-armed version with Gabizo wingtip jets called the Trident II SE was ordered for operational use, but budget cuts saw its cancellation. The Trident II was nudging Mach 2 when the programme was axed in 1958.

SPECIFICATIONS (Trident II)

CREW:	one
POWERPLANT:	one 22.24kN (5000lb-thrust) Rolls-Royce Nene turbojet, two 3.92kN (882lb-thrust) Turboméca Marboré turbojets and one 4.9kN (1102lb-thrust) SEPR 481 rocket
MAX SPEED:	Mach 1.55
MAX ALTITUDE:	16,764m (55,000ft)
SPAN:	7.56m (24ft 10in)
LENGTH:	14.36m (47ft 2in)
HEIGHT:	2.83m (9ft 4in)
WEIGHT:	loaded 5056kg (11,144lb)

Powered by three turbojets and a rocket, the Trident was a high-performance machine, but was regarded as too complicated for a squadron pilot.

The Trident's nose capsule was replaced by a conventional ejection seat in the Trident II.

The wingtip nacelles contained Marboré II turbojets, and there was a three-chambered SEPR 481 rocket mounted in the tail.

The vertical fin was an all-moving surface with no separate rudder.

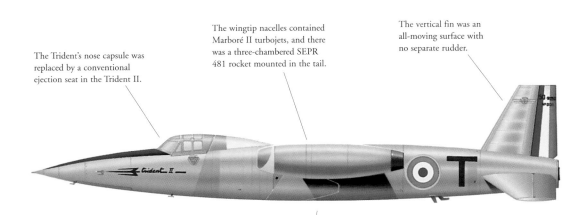

The fuselage centre section had tanks for both the jets and the rocket engines, which used nitric acid and Furaline as fuel.

SNCASO TRITON (1946)

Designed in secret during the German occupation, the Triton ('Newt') was built by Sud-Ouest (SNCASO) almost as soon as the war was over. Because the planned French Rateau turbojet was not ready, the Triton began its flying career in November 1946 powered by a modified Junkers Jumo 004B as used in the Messerschmitt Me 262. With this engine it was seriously underpowered and barely flew at all. The Rateau engine never emerged, and Rolls-Royce Nene engines were fitted to the other four prototypes. Many problems were encountered with the airframes up until the test programme ended in November 1950, but the Triton gave the test pilots of the Centre de Essais en Vol (CEV) their first jet experience, which was to stand them in good stead when more advanced equipment came along.

SPECIFICATIONS

CREW:	two
POWERPLANT:	one 21.6kN (4850lb-thrust) Rolls-Royce Nene 101 turbojet engine
MAX SPEED:	954km/h (593mph)
MAX ALTITUDE:	11,887m (39,000ft)
SPAN:	10.56m (34ft 8in)
LENGTH:	10.37m (34ft 1in)
HEIGHT:	3.01m (10ft 2in)
WEIGHT:	loaded 4550kg (10,032lb)

The Triton became the first indigenous French turbojet-powered aircraft. Its performance was not particularly stunning, but it helped French industry, engineers and pilots increase their knowledge of jets and begin to catch up on the US and UK after World War II.

The two-man crew consisted of a pilot and a flight engineer, an unusual but cautious approach to the unknown territory of jet flight. The pilot on the first flight was Daniel Rastel.

The third of the five Tritons is preserved at the Musée de l'Air. Its windscreen was extended forwards compared to the original configuration.

As originally built the Triton's intake was set low in the nose and the intake trunking passed between the cockpit seats. The Nene-powered models had additional 'elephant ear' intakes behind the cockpit.

SUKHOI SU-9 AND SU-11 (1946)

The capture of German equipment and scientists helped the USSR's aircraft industry catch up with jet development quickly after World War II. Several approaches were taken, but Pavel Sukhoi's was to base his Su-9 fighter closely, but not slavishly, on the layout of the Messerschmitt Me 262. Su-9 flight tests began in 1946. Some sources say in August; others in November. Its first public appearance was at Tushino on 3 July 1947. By this time the improved Su-11 was in test, having first flown on 28 May. The Su-11 had two much larger diameter Lyulka TR-1 turbojets. The Soviet Air Force test centre recommended immediate production of the Su-11, but several influential figures (including rival designer Yakovlev) convinced the Kremlin that the Su-11 was nothing but a copy of the Me 262 and dangerous besides. Stalin cancelled the Su-11 in favour of the inferior Yak-15.

SPECIFICATIONS (Su-11)

CREW:	one
POWERPLANT:	two 12.77kN (2870lb-thrust) Lyulka TR-1 turbojet engines
MAX SPEED:	565mph (910km/h)
MAX ALTITUDE:	unknown
SPAN:	11.80m (38ft 8in)
LENGTH:	10.57m (34ft 7in)
HEIGHT:	3.72m (12ft 2in)
WEIGHT:	loaded 6350kg (14,000lb)

The Su-9 and Su-11 were probably the best of the first-generation Soviet jets, but were dismissed unfairly as copies of Nazi technology. The Su-9 and Su-11 designations were reused by Sukhoi for two later single-engined designs with the NATO reporting name 'Fishpot'.

The Su-9's engines were copies of the Me 262's Jumo 004s and the canopy was very similar, but the other shapes, including the wing (which had no sweepback), were quite different.

The Su-11 was the first aircraft powered by Lyulka jets. This design bureau remains in business today as one of the main engine makers in Russia.

The Su-9 had one of the first ejection seats used in the USSR.

The armament of the Su-9 and Su-11 was the standard early Soviet jet fit of two one 37mm (1.46in) and two 23mm (0.91in) cannon.

SCALE TESTBEDS

Before committing to an expensive aircraft project, it has on occasion been thought wise to test the waters with a aerodynamic or systems testbed, often sub-scale to the intended first prototype.

New wing planforms such as the complex deltas of the Concorde and Tu-144 supersonic transports and the 'double delta' of the Saab Draken proved particularly suitable for this approach. In several cases, including the Avro 707 and Handley-Page HP.88, which both supported the RAF's 'V-bomber' programme, construction and flight trials of the testbed aircraft were only just ahead of the full size machine.

The demonstrators for France's ACX (Avion de Combat Experimental) and the European EAP (Experimental Aircraft Programme) were unusual in both being slightly larger than the production aircraft that followed, the Dassault Rafale C and the Eurofighter Typhoon respectively. Computer modelling reduced the unknowns in the basic characteristics, but the fine-tuning of the computerized flight control systems was a greater task. Evolution and miniaturizzation of the FCS contributed to the smaller size of the production fighters.

Left: *The Handley Page H.P.115 contributed greatly to the development of Concorde, exploring low-speed handling characteristics.*

AVRO 707 *(1949)*

The delta wing offered many performance advantages at high speeds, but low-speed handling was an unknown area when the Avro Vulcan bomber was being designed, hence the need for a scaled-down testbed to explore this end of the envelope. The Avro 707 flew 4 September 1949, but unfortunately crashed fatally on the 30th. After a delay it was replaced by the slightly longer 707B, which had an ejection seat. Two 707As for high-speed research followed, with wing-root intakes and a wing planform more representative of the Vulcan. The 707C was a dual-seat trainer, designed to help convert pilots to the Vulcan, but which spent most of its time on control system research. The first 707A was fitted with a kinked leading edge, which became the pattern for the 'Phase 2' wing of the later Vulcans. In 1956 this aircraft was sold to Australia and spent a further decade there on low-speed flight research.

SPECIFICATIONS

CREW:	one
POWERPLANT:	one 187kN (42,000lb-thrust) Pratt & Whitney F119-PW-611C afterburning turbofan engine
MAX SPEED:	Mach 1.8
MAX ALTITUDE:	13,716m (45,000ft)
SPAN:	13.12m (43ft)
LENGTH:	15.52m (50ft 11in)
HEIGHT:	4.60m (15ft 2in)
WEIGHT:	loaded 17,485m (38,549lb)

More 707s were built than most other purely experimental aircraft. They flew slightly too late to have much effect on Vulcan development. Both 707As and the 707C are preserved in museums.

The 707 and 707B had Gloster Meteor canopies and many other parts from other aircraft, notably undercarriage components.

The 707 and 707B had an intake above the rear fuselage. Turbulence over the canopy reduced the airflow to the engine and the 707As and 707C were built with Vulcan-style intakes.

The 707 and 707C appeared in natural metal finish, whereas the 707B was gloss blue and the 707As were in salmon pink and later high-visibility orange.

BELL XV-15 *(1977)*

The XV-15 programme began as a US Army/NASA effort in 1973 as a proof of concept craft for a production tiltrotor transport, which later became the V-22 Osprey. Two XV-15s were built, the first flying on 3 May 1977. One was demonstrated at the 1995 Paris Air Show alongside a V-22 Osprey. Flight testing continued until 1998 and eventually encompassed 530 flight hours in the hands of more than 185 pilots.

The second aircraft was brought out of retirement and served as a demonstrator and proof of concept vehicle for the smaller civilian Bell-Agusta BA.609 tiltrotor transport. This aircraft eventually logged more than 700 hours, and its final flight was made to the National Air and Space Museum's Steven F. Udvar-Hazy Center in 2003.

The XV-15 set the groundwork for the V-22 Osprey, which has had a lengthy gestation, but has finally become the first tiltrotor design to enter service.

SPECIFICATIONS

CREW:	two
POWERPLANT:	two 1156kW (1550hp) Lycoming T-53 turboshaft engines
MAX SPEED:	550km/h (342mph)
MAX ALTITUDE:	8800m (28,873ft)
SPAN:	9.8m (32ft 2in)
LENGTH:	12.8 m (42ft 1in)
HEIGHT:	VTOL mode 4.67m (15ft 4in)
WEIGHT:	loaded 4574kg (10,083lb)

In a long career, the XV-15 proved the concept of the tiltrotor for the V-22 programme, trained V-22 pilots and later did the same for the Bell-Agusta 609 civilian tiltrotor.

The XV-15 could take off vertically or make a rolling take-off with the nacelles tilted forwards. Once airborne, it transitioned to aeroplane mode with the nacelles fully forward.

The XV-15 had a nominal capacity for nine passengers in the cabin, but there were no side windows or other comforts.

The transmission system could compensate for an engine failure by spreading the power of the remaining engine to both rotors. The transmissions were mounted in the nacelles with the engines.

BRITISH AEROSPACE EAP (1986)

From studies in the early 1980s into an agile combat aircraft (ACA), British Aerospace, mainly using private money, developed a demonstrator under the Experimental Aircraft Programme banner. The aircraft itself became known as the EAP. The rationale of the EAP was integration of several new and experimental technologies in a single airframe in support of the European Fighter Aircraft (EFA) programme. The quadruplex fly-by-wire (FBW) control system was first tested on a Jaguar modified with balance weights to be inherently unstable without FBW. The EAP's close-coupled canard configuration is also naturally unstable.

The EAP first flew on 8 August 1986, piloted by Dave Eagles, and reached Mach 1.1. In the course of 259 test flights up to May 1991, the EAP gathered vital data for the EFA project, later to become the Eurofighter Typhoon.

SPECIFICATIONS

CREW:	one
POWERPLANT:	two 75.62kN (17,000lb-thrust) Turbo-Union B.199-3AR Mk 104AD turbofan engines
MAX SPEED:	over 2124 km/h (1320mph)
MAX ALTITUDE:	unknown
SPAN:	11.77m (38ft 7in)
LENGTH:	14.70m (48ft 3in)
HEIGHT:	5.52m (18ft 2in)
WEIGHT:	loaded 14,515kg (32,000lb)

Despite its similar appearance, the EAP was not a true prototype of the Eurofighter, but served as a flying testbed for many of the technologies that would eventually find their way into the Typhoon.

The EAP's tailfin was the same as a Tornado GR.1s, and the engines were those used in the Tornado F.3 fighter.

The advanced cockpit included multi-function displays and a voice-activated control system. The latter was developed for use in the Typhoon.

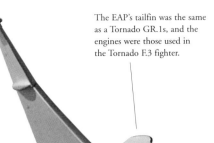

Construction materials included carbon-fibre composites, titanium and aluminium-lithium alloys. The wings and foreplanes were the largest carbon-fibre components.

The intake lower lip was hinged downwards to give better airflow at high angles of attack. This idea was not adapted for the Eurofighter, partly because of its high radar return.

DASSAULT RAFALE A (1986)

The ACX (Avion de Combat Experimental) programme began in 1980 as a Mirage 2000 replacement for the French Air Force and to supplant the French navy's Crusader and Super Etendard. The ACX would be a generation ahead of the Mirage 2000, with new engines, new avionics including voice command, and a degree of stealth capability, so two ACX demonstrator aircraft were ordered. One was cancelled, but the other, piloted by Guy Mitaux-Maurouard, first flew on 4 July 1986 with General Electric F404 engines as an interim measure. By now the proposed fighter was named the Rafale (Squall), and the demonstrator was renamed the Rafale A. One F404 was replaced by a SNECMA M88 in 1990 and the Rafale A carried on to make 865 test flights by the time it was retired in 1994.

SPECIFICATIONS
(as first flown)

CREW:	one
POWERPLANT:	two 71.17kN (16,000lb-thrust) General Electric F404-GE-400 afterburning turbofans
MAX SPEED:	Mach 1.4
MAX ALTITUDE:	unknown
SPAN:	11.20m (36ft 9in)
LENGTH:	15.80m (51ft 10in)
HEIGHT:	5.20m (17ft 0in)
WEIGHT:	maximum 20,000kg (41,000lb)

A close contemporary of Britain's EAP, the ACX demonstrator came into its own when France split from the EFA project in 1986. The ACX/Rafale A laid the groundwork for the Rafale M, which entered service before the Eurofighter Typhoon.

Although it had no arrestor hook or other naval equipment, the Rafale A made approaches to France's aircraft carriers to test the handling of the future Rafale M naval version.

Delays in the SNECMA M88 engine saw the Rafale A fly initially with F404s as used in the F/A-18 Hornet. One of the development M88-2 engines was flown in the Rafale A during the second half of its flying career.

Unusually for a programme demonstrator aircraft, the Rafale was slightly larger than the production version. Otherwise its appearance was very close to the production Rafale C.

DORNIER SEASTAR (1984)

To meet a perceived need for a new technology utility seaplane, an offshoot of Dornier GmbH was formed as Claudius Dornier Seastar in 1982. On 17 August 1984 the CD-1 Seastar, D-ICDS made its first flight. It suffered damage in an accident and was retired in 1985. The company reorganized and relocated, and produced two improved CD-2 prototypes in 1987 and 1988. These differed in having a composite (rather than metal) wing, which was strong enough not to need external bracing. The first CD-2 was also registered D-ICDS and the second was D-ICKS. This had Dornier's patented TNT (*tragflügels neuer technologie*) advanced supercritical wing as used on the Do 228 and 328 (and the Do 24TT). Various orders were announced, but not realized. A proposed deal to produce the CD-2 in Malaysia under the Dornier Seastar banner fell through in 1994.

SPECIFICATIONS

CREW:	two
POWERPLANT:	two 517kW (650hp) PT6A-135A turboprop engines
MAX SPEED:	324km/h (212mph)
MAX ALTITUDE:	8535m (28,000ft)
SPAN:	17.74m (58ft 2in)
LENGTH:	12.70m (41ft 8in)
HEIGHT:	4.83m (15ft 10in)
WEIGHT:	loaded 4600kg (10,141lb)

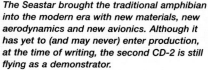

The Seastar brought the traditional amphibian into the modern era with new materials, new aerodynamics and new avionics. Although it has yet to (and may never) enter production, at the time of writing, the second CD-2 is still flying as a demonstrator.

The Seastar is powered by two PT6 turboprops mounted in tandem above the wing. The fuel tanks are in the sponsons on the fuselage sides, which also provide stability in the water.

The standard Seastar's cabin had accommodation for 12 passengers in four rows of three seats. Alternate layouts included a six-seat VIP cabin or a Medevac fit for six stretchers.

D-ICDS

seastar

GÖPPINGEN GÖ 9 *(1940)*

In 1937 Claudius Dornier patented the idea of a tail-mounted pusher propeller with a mid-mounted engine, and later commissioned glider makers Schempp-Hirth at Göppingen to build a testbed aircraft. The resulting Göppingen Gö 9 first flew in early 1940, towed aloft by a Dornier 17 bomber. The Gö 9's aerodynamics were scaled down from of those of the Do 17, but that aircraft's two engines were replaced by a single unit driving the propeller with a long extension shaft. After a number of towed flights the Gö 9 proved able to take off under its own power.

The programme ended in 1941 and the eventual fate of the Gö 9 is unknown, but based on its findings Dornier developed the Do-335 Pfiel, which had both pusher and tractor propellers and was the fastest piston-engined fighter of the war. The Schempp-Hirth firm survives today and is one of the premier manufacturers of sport gliders.

SPECIFICATIONS

CREW:	one
POWERPLANT:	one 60kW (80hp) Hirth I M60 R air-cooled in-line engine
MAX SPEED:	220km/h (137mph)
MAX ALTITUDE:	unknown
SPAN:	7.2m (23ft 8in)
LENGTH:	6.8m (22ft 4in)
HEIGHT:	unknown
WEIGHT:	loaded 720kg (1587lb)

Essentially a glider based on the layout of the Do 17 bomber, the Gö 9 served as a testbed for the propulsion system of the Do 335 fighter, pictured.

The Gö-9 was essentially a Do 17 scaled down to 1:2.5 scale and fitted with a pusher propeller. This arrangement reduced drag and allowed a good performance for an aircraft with a small motor.

The engine was mounted just behind the cockpit, using a long extension shaft that ran down the rear fuselage to drive the four-bladed pusher propeller.

The cruciform tail unit needed a small wheel on the bottom fin to protect it. The aircraft sat back on this wheel when no pilot was aboard.

HANDLEY PAGE H.P.115 *(1961)*

T he H.P.115 was designed to explore the low-speed end of the flight regime of slender delta-winged aircraft. In particular it flew in support of the proposed British supersonic transport, later to become the Anglo-French Concorde. First flying on 17 August 1961 in the hands of J.M. Henderson, the H.P.115 disproved predictions that it would be hard to handle and in fact was very well liked by its test pilots, demonstrating rapid changes of bank at low speeds without loss of control. Speeds as low as 111km/h (69mph) with 30-degree angle of incidence were safely achieved. Despite a couple of minor accidents, the H.P.115 had a very long career for a research aircraft, flying until 1974 when it was retired. One test series used noise generators in several places to measure the noise patterns of a slender delta. Today it is displayed at Yeovilton, Somerset, alongside the BAC 221 and a prototype Concorde.

SPECIFICATIONS

CREW:	one
POWERPLANT:	one 8.45kN (1900lb-thrust) Bristol Siddeley Viper BSV9 turbojet engine
MAX SPEED:	324km/h (201mph)
MAX ALTITUDE:	unknown
SPAN:	6.10m (20ft 0in)
LENGTH:	15.33m (50ft 4in)
HEIGHT:	3.90m (12ft 9in)
WEIGHT:	loaded 2291kg (5050lb)

The HP.115 was a support aircraft used in the development of Concorde. Not the world's prettiest aircraft, it contributed greatly to the handing of long, slender delta-winged aircraft in take-off and landing configuration.

Like many experimental aircraft, the HP.115's fuel supply was limited, giving enough for about 30 minutes' endurance.

The undercarriage was fixed in the down position and was adapted from a Percival Prentice (maingear) and Miles Aerovan nosegear.

The wing had an extraordinary 74.7 degrees sweep and an aspect ratio of 1.0. The leading edges were made of plywood so that different degrees of camber could be tested by swapping in new extensions. This facility was never used, and only one configuration was tested.

HANDLEY PAGE HP.88 (1951)

Built to a British government specification, the HP.88 was intended to test the aerodynamics of the crescent wing intended for the HP Type 80 bomber, later named the Victor. To create the HP.88, a modified Supermarine 510 fuselage was married to a scaled-down version of the HP.80 wing. The work was contracted to Blackburn Aircraft, and Blackburn pilot G.R. Parker made the first flight on 21 June 1951. Some problems were found with stability in pitch, and the aircraft was almost impossible to control above 255 knots (472km/h; 293mph). A plumb bob damper and some strips of angle bracket were added to the tail correct this. After about only 30 flights, the HP.88 was lost when it broke up during a low-level pass at Stansted, north of London, killing the pilot Douglas Broomfield.

SPECIFICATIONS

CREW:	one
POWERPLANT:	one 22.24kN (5000lb-thrust) Rolls-Royce Nene 2 R.N.2 turbojet engine
MAX SPEED:	Estimated Mach 0.9
MAX ALTITUDE:	unknown
SPAN:	12.19m (40ft 0in)
LENGTH:	12.16m (39ft 10in)
HEIGHT:	tail up 3.86m (12ft 8in)
WEIGHT:	loaded 6641kg (14,640lb)

A very short career was the main achievement of the HP.88. Only 28 sorties and 14 flight hours were logged before its destruction, and as a consequence it was unable to contribute much to Victor development.

The HP.88's one-third scale crescent wing was not actually very representative of the Victor's, having a different planform and control layout. The utility of the HP.88 would have to be questionable, even if it had lasted longer.

The HP.88's fuselage was that of the Supermarine 510 modified with a new wing mounting and large hydraulically-powered airbrakes aft of the wing.

A large bullet fairing was mounted at the fin-tailplane junction. The probe extending from it measured yaw forces. At the rear of the bullet was a brake parachute housing.

LOCKHEED XST 'HAVE BLUE' (1977)

To prove the Lockheed 'Skunk Works' theories on low observable (LO) technologies prior to committing to a production 'stealth' combat aircraft, on 1 December 1977 the XST (Experimental Survivable Testbed), built under the code name 'Have Blue', was test flown in great secrecy by Lockheed test pilot Bill Park. Due to its odd shape, the XST needed fully computer-controlled fly-by-wire. The flight control system was modified from an F-16s, but could handle inherent instability in three axes rather than two. The first Have Blue was lost in an accident on its 36th flight in May 1978, and the second crashed in July 1979 on its 52nd flight. Both pilots made safe ejections, and the wrecks were buried to preserve their secrets. In November 1978 the go-ahead was given for the full-scale development of a combat-capable version under the code name 'Senior Trend'. This became the F-117A Nighthawk, which first flew in June 1981.

SPECIFICATIONS

CREW:	one
POWERPLANT:	two 13.1kN (2950lb-thrust) General Electric J85-GE-4A turbojet engines
MAX SPEED:	966km/h (600mph)
MAX ALTITUDE:	unknown
SPAN:	6.86m (22ft 6in)
LENGTH:	14.40m (47ft 3in)
HEIGHT:	2.30m (7ft 6.25in)
WEIGHT:	loaded 5670kg (12,500lb)

Smaller and lighter than the F-117 that followed, the Have Blue prototypes were used only to evaluate the radar cross-section characteristics of the design. These tests led to considerable revisions of the F-117.

The first XST had an unusual 'splinter' camouflage pattern designed to hide the faceted surfaces. Neither of the two examples had any weapons bay or tactical equipment.

The wing sweep was an extremely sharp 72.5 degrees, greater than that on the production F-117. The tailfins were canted inwards and mounted further forward than on the Nighthawk.

The main landing gear was taken from a Fairchild A-10, the engines came from a Rockwell T-2B Buckeye, and the instruments and the ejector seat were surplus Northrop F-5 parts.

MIKOYAN-GUREVICH MIG-21I ANALOG (1968)

To test the new wing layout of the proposed Tupolev supersonic transport (SST), the Soviet authorities commissioned a modified MiG-21 to act as a testbed with a scaled-down wing. Known as the MiG-21I, or 'Analog', it had an ogival delta wing which replaced the delta wing and swept tailplane of the standard MiG-21S from which the two MiG-21Is were converted on the production line. O.V. Gudkov made the first flight of the first Analog (the 21I/1) on 18 April 1968.

As with a number of similar aircraft, delays in building, flying and evaluating the Analog meant that it had little real effect on the design of the Tu-144 SST. The Tu-144 itself flew in December 1968, accompanied by an Analog. Tu-144 pilots first flew the Analog to experience the handling characteristics of the ogival wing. The first aircraft crashed in 1970, but the slightly different 21I/2 survived for preservation at Monino, Russia.

SPECIFICATIONS

CREW:	one
POWERPLANT:	one 63.65kN (14,308lb-thrust) R-13F-300 afterburning turbojet
MAX SPEED:	2100km/h (1305mph)
MAX ALTITUDE:	20,000m (65,620m)
SPAN:	8.15m (26ft 9in)
LENGTH:	12.29m (40ft 4in)
HEIGHT:	4.71m (15ft 5in)
WEIGHT:	maximum 9000kg (19,842lb)

In profile looking much like a standard MiG-21, in planform the Analog showed its sophisticated double delta wing. This Mach 2 aircraft performed the same function as did the BAC.221 in the Concorde programme.

The second Analog (the 21I/2) had an enlarged leading-edge root extension (LERX). The trailing edge of the wing was comprised of eight small elevons.

The new wing had a sweep on the forward portion of 78 degrees and 55 degrees to the rear. The wing was extremely thin, requiring that the elevon actuators be mounted in external fairings.

To study airflow over the wing, extensive tests were made with cotton tufts on the upper surfaces. Cameras behind the cockpit and in the fintip were used to film the movements of these tufts.

The Shuttle Transportation System (STS) involves three forms of flight: as a rocket; weightless flight in the earth's orbit; and as the world's largest glider when it returns to the atmosphere. In order to test this critical mission phase, Rockwell built the unpowered OV-101 Orbiter Vehicle for NASA in 1976. Originally to be named Constitution, the OV-101 became *Enterprise* after a campaign by *Star Trek* fans. To simulate the flight of a shuttle after re-entry, *Enterprise* was carried aloft and released by a modified Boeing 747. The Shuttle/747 combination made three high-speed taxi runs, five 'captive-inactive' flights (to test the aerodynamics of the composite aircraft), three captive-active flights (where the shuttle's systems were activated), then five free flights. The first of these was made on 12 August 1977, with the crew comprising Fred Haise and Gordon Fullerton.

SPECIFICATIONS

CREW:	two
POWERPLANT:	none
MAX SPEED:	unknown
MAX ALTITUDE:	(dropping altitude) 6949m (22,800ft)
SPAN:	23.79m (78ft 1in)
LENGTH:	without boom 37.24m (122ft 3in)
HEIGHT:	10.55m (34ft 8in)
WEIGHT:	68,100kg (150,000lb)

The Enterprise *was a full-scale testbed for the Space Shuttle's aerodynamics and many of its systems. Its main function was to prove the feasibility of the STS as a glider, with its one shot at a landing. It was also used in fit checks of the external tank and the procedure for assembling the entire system before launch.*

A large aerodynamic fairing was mounted on the shuttle's tail to protect the 747's fin from disturbed airflow. This was removed for two of the five free flights.

As a pure aerodynamic test vehicle, *Enterprise* had no engines or equipment for space flight. It was retired to the National Air and Space Museum in 1983. Parts were removed for testing in conjunction with the investigation into the 2003 *Columbia* disaster.

Enterprise was flown on the 747 to the 1979 Paris Air Show and to other events. NASA's two 747 Shuttle Carrier Aircraft (SCAs) are used to move the production orbiters after landings away from the Kennedy Space Center in Florida.

SAAB 210 'LILL DRAKEN' (1952)

Scale versions of the wings of Saab's J-29 Tunnan and J-32 Lansen fighters had been tested on a piston-engined Safir trainer, but this was not practicable for the supersonic J35 Draken, which was being designed to meet a 1949 requirement. It was decided to build a piloted testbed of about 70 per cent scale to establish the characteristics of this wing. The Saab 210 'Lill Draken' (Little Dragon) first flew in January 1952 piloted by Bengt Olow. The design of the full-size J 35 Draken was frozen in March, and the 210 continued to carry out many test flights in support of the Draken programme. Initially flown with a blunt nose that just protruded ahead of the intakes, the Lill Draken was modified to become the Saab 210-2 with a longer nose and more representative intakes.

SPECIFICATIONS

CREW:	one
POWERPLANT:	one 4.45kN (1000lb-thrust) Armstrong Siddeley Adder AS.A.1 turbojet
MAX SPEED:	unknown
MAX ALTITUDE:	unknown
SPAN:	6.35m (20ft 10in)
LENGTH:	8.80m (28ft 10in)
HEIGHT:	2.78m (9ft 1in)
WEIGHT:	unknown

Four years before the first flight of the J 35 Draken in October 1955, the Saab 210 proved the suitability of its configuration. The 210 flew into 1956, then was retired for eventual display in the Swedish Air Force Museum.

144

The fin was reduced in height during tests. Many jet fighters started with inadequate fin area, which later needed to be increased for better stability.

Long pitot heads were carried under each wing on the 210-1, but were replaced by a single nose-mounted probe on the 210-2.

The Lill Draken's undercarriage wheels remained partly exposed in the lower fuselage when retracted.

SHORT S.31 (HALF-SCALE STIRLING) (1938)

The handling characteristics of giant four-engined bombers were something of an unknown when Short's S.29 Stirling was commissioned. To answer various aerodynamic questions, a half-scale testbed called the S.31 was designed and was flown on 19 September 1938 by John Lankester Parker and Hugh Gordon. The S.31 had a long take-off run and a tendency to swing to the right. In the air it 'handled like a fighter'. The short, wide wings gave a good rate of roll in particular.

An increase in wing incidence for better take-off performance was called for, but was too complicated a modification; the mainwheel legs were extended to give the same effect. Longitudinal control changes were made at the same time. Horn-balanced elevators were trialled, but a larger tailplane with conventional elevators was the eventual solution.

SPECIFICATIONS

CREW:	two
POWERPLANT:	four 85kW (114hp) Pobjoy Niagara radial piston engines
MAX SPEED:	296km/h (184mph)
MAX ALTITUDE:	unknown
SPAN:	15.12m (49ft 7in)
LENGTH:	13.29m (43ft 7in)
HEIGHT:	unknown
WEIGHT:	loaded 2585kg (5700lb)

One of a handful of wartime sub-scale testbeds, the S.31 worked out some of the design issues for the RAF's first modern heavy bomber. The Stirling itself turned out to be somewhat of a disappointment.

In contrast to the all-metal Stirling, the S.31 had a plywood-covered wing, plywood-covered semi-monocoque fuselage and all-wooden tail unit.

The S.31 was originally built with 67kW (90hp) Pobjoy Niagara III radials; these were later replaced by 86kW (115kW) Niagara IVs.

The Stirling bomber had three gun turrets and a crew of seven. The half-scale S.31 had no armament and just two pilots.

The Stirling prototype itself flew in May 1939, giving little chance for the S.31 to influence its design. The S.31 was scrapped in 1943.

SHORT SB.5 (1952)

Teddy Petter's Lightning was the highest-performance all-British fighter. It was preceded by the P.1, which trialled the unusual wing layout and engine arrangement. The P.1 itself was intended to rely on data from the low-performance SB.5, a research aircraft commissioned by the Royal Aeronautical Establishment (RAE) and built by Shorts in Belfast. The RAE did not trust Petter's calculations for the P.1 and was particularly sceptical of his low-set tailplane. The SB.5 had a fixed undercarriage and could only explore low-speed handling. From 2 December 1952 it was tested with several wing configurations and either a low-set or a T-tail. The SB.5 was rebuilt several times with the wing set at 50, 60 and 69 degrees. Eventually it validated Petter's original layout, but had little direct influence on the design of the P.1.

SPECIFICATIONS

CREW:	one
POWERPLANT:	one 16.01kN (3600lb-thrust) Rolls-Royce Derwent turbojet engine
MAX SPEED:	350 knots
MAX ALTITUDE:	3048m (10,000ft)
SPAN:	(50 degree sweep) 10.72m (35ft 2in)
LENGTH:	14.55m (47ft 9in)
HEIGHT:	(high tail) 5.28m (17ft 4in)
WEIGHT:	max loaded 5897kg (13,000lb)

Delays in completing the SB.5 did not slow the P.1, and the 20 months between their first flights did not allow for any significant changes to the latter. Nevertheless, the SB.5 contributed to the understanding of highly swept wings at low speeds.

In 1958 the engine was upgraded from a Derwent engine to a 22.24kN (5000lb-thrust) Bristol Orpheus. At the same time the wing was swept to 69 degrees and a Martin Baker ejection seat was fitted.

The SB.5 ended its career at the Empire Test Pilot's School (ETPS) in 1967 and is now preserved at the RAF Museum, Cosford, in Shropshire with both its tails.

The SB.5 had the same basic configuration as the P.1, but a fixed undercarriage. The two large probes protruding from the intake mounted a pitot tube and pitch and yaw sensors.

SNCASO SO.4000 VAUTOUR I (1951)

French regional manufacturer Sud-Ouest offered the two-seat twin-engine Vautour (Vulture) for an air force requirement for a medium bomber. Two half research aircraft were built to test the configuration of the S.O 4000. These were the SO.M1 and M2, but they had little in common with the final bomber. The M1 was a glider, and the M2 had a Rolls-Royce Derwent engine. Testing took place in 1949. The SO.4000 itself first flew on 16 March 1951 in the hands of Jacques Guignard. This was also its last flight, as it proved to be very underpowered and unstable. The programme was abandoned for budgetary reasons and because the design was basically obsolete by the time it was flown. To meet a revised 1951 requirement, the design team completely revised the configuration and came up with the Vautour II (the suffix was rarely used). This became a very successful bomber and night-fighter.

SPECIFICATIONS

CREW:	two
POWERPLANT:	two 22.16kN (4982lb-thrust) Hispano-Suiza (Rolls-Royce) Nene 102 turbojet engines
MAX SPEED:	850km/h (528mph)
MAX ALTITUDE:	estimated 12,802m (42,000ft)
SPAN:	17.86m (58ft 6in)
LENGTH:	19.75m (64ft 9in)
HEIGHT:	unknown
WEIGHT:	maximum 22,000kg (48,510lb)

Although completely unsuccessful, the SO.4000 qualifies as the first French jet bomber. A return to the drawing board created the Vautour II, which had absolutely nothing in common with its predecessor.

The proposed armament was up to 1814kg (4000lb) of bombs in an internal bay. Defensive weapons were proposed as 20mm (0.79in) cannon in wingtip barbettes.

The small fuel tanks were fitted above the centre section. The combat radius would have been about 610km (380 miles).

The main landing gear was so large that it prevented the wing being used for fuel tanks. The huge wheel wells also reduced the strength of the wing.

VTOL

Almost nothing in aerospace has created as many acronyms as the quest for practical Vertical Take-Off and Landing (VTOL) aircraft. These include STOVL (Short Take-Off and Vertical Landing, STOBAR (Short Take-Off But Arrested Landing) and V/STOL (Vertical/Short Take-Off and Landing).

The technology to achieve this has included tilt-engines, tilt-fans, tilt-wings, lift fans, lift engines and puffer jets. For the less demanding task of shortening the take-off and landing run, blown flaps, upper surface blowing and jet flaps have all been tried, generally involving the ducting of engine air over the flying surfaces to convince the aircraft it is flying faster than it really is.

Many types of helicopter have been produced, but their speed limitations have inspired many variations, such as compound and rigid-rotor helicopters and ramjet-driven rotors to boost performance. Non-rotorcraft VTOL aircraft offered the hope of higher speeds and more useful load, but altogether have been less successful. Of approximately 45 different non-helicopter VTO designs that reached the hardware stage since 1950, only three have, pending the F-35B Joint Strike Fighter, ever reached service – the Yak-36, Harrier, and V-22 Osprey.

Left: *One of the more promising VTOL designs of the 1960s was the three-engined VFW-Fokker VAK 191B.*

BELL X-14 *(1957)*

The only open-cockpit X-Plane, the Bell X-14 made its first (tethered) hovering test flight in the hands of company pilot David Howe on 19 February 1957. Unlike most 1950s vertical take-off machines, the X-14 was not a 'tail sitter', but demonstrated horizontal attitude, vertical take-off, hover, transition to forward flight and vertical landing. Movable vanes in the jetpipes vectored the thrust through the jet nozzles on the centreline to allow low-speed and hovering flight. In addition to NASA pilots, 25 other US and foreign pilots were to experience VTOL flight in the X-14. Because of its reaction control system, one role was use in lunar lander research for the Apollo space programme. After a hard landing in 1981, the only significant mishap it suffered in a 24-year career, the X-14 was retired to the US Army Aviation Museum in Alabama.

SPECIFICATIONS (X-14)

CREW:	one
POWERPLANT:	two 8.45kN (1900lb-thrust) Armstrong-Siddeley Viper 8 turbojet engines
MAX SPEED:	277km/h (172mph)
MAX ALTITUDE:	5485m (18,000ft)
SPAN:	10.30m (33ft 9in)
LENGTH:	7.92m (26ft 0in)
HEIGHT:	2.68m (8ft 10ft)
WEIGHT:	maximum 1936kg (4629lb)

Extremely long-lived for an X-plane, the X-14 proved the feasibility of vectored-thrust VTOL. Much of the data it collected was used in designing the P.1127, precursor to the Harrier.

In hovering flight the ailerons were ineffective, so compressed air nozzles in the wingtips provided roll control.

The X-14 was largely made of surplus Beech aircraft parts. The wings, ailerons and landing gear of a Bonanza were used, as was the tailplane from a T-34 Mentor.

The engine changes and other modifications such as lengthened landing gear saw the designation change from X-14 to X-14A and then X-14B.

The original Viper engines were soon replaced by 11.92kN (2680lb-thrust) General Electric J85-GE-5s when it was delivered to NASA. These in turn were later changed for J85-GE-19s of 13.45kN (3018lb-thrust).

BELL X-22 *(1966)*

To meet a US Navy requirement for a VTOL research aircraft with tilting ducted propellers, Bell built two Model D-2127s, also known as the X-22. Flight tests began on 17 March 1966, but the first prototype was damaged beyond repair in a heavy landing on 8 August. The second flew in January 1967 and soon demonstrated full transitions to forward flight. Problems with the retractable landing gear were never solved, and the wheels were later locked down. The X-22 was used in tests for the three main US services, for the US Federal Aviation Administration (FAA) and for NASA. Its last user was the Cornell Aeronautical Laboratory, which flew it for 10 years on VTOL research until 1984, when it was retired. It can be found today at the Niagara Aerospace Museum at Niagara Falls, New York.

SPECIFICATIONS

CREW:	two
POWERPLANT:	four 932kW (1250hp) General Electric YT58-GE-8D turboshaft engines
MAX SPEED:	509km/h (316mph)
MAX ALTITUDE:	8475m (27,800ft)
SPAN:	11.96m (39ft 3in)
LENGTH:	12.06m (39ft 7in)
HEIGHT:	5.99m (19ft 8in)
WEIGHT:	maximum 8172kg (18,016lb)

The X-22 did not lead to a production tilt-fan aircraft, but proved very useful on general VTOL research, simulating operations of theoretical aircraft rather than just ones of its specific configuration.

The four ducted fans were connected to a common drive shaft. The engines themselves were in the wing roots of the rear stub wing.

The X-22 had a variable stability system incorporated from the beginning. Adjusting this system allowed the simulation of many different types of VTOL aircraft, including the AV-8B Harrier.

Elevons mounted behind each ducted fan were the only control surfaces. There was no rudder, as all control movements were made by tilting the ducts and altering the propeller pitch.

BOEING QSRA (1978)

In 1978 under a NASA programme Boeing modified a twin-turboprop de Havilland Canada DHC-5 (C-8A) Buffalo into the four-jet Quiet Short-Haul Research Aircraft (QSRA). The aircraft was 63-13687, the second Buffalo built, and was given the NASA registration N715NA. The two turbo-prop engines were replaced with four jets that discharged their exhaust over the top of the highly modified wing, making use of the Coanda effect for extra lift. The programme's objectives were to achieve short take-off performance and low noise. Flight tests began at NASA's Ames facility (Moffett Field), California, in August 1978. The QSRA required only a 457m (1500ft) runway and noise levels of 90 EPNdB (equivalent perceived noise) were achieved, less than any other jet STOL transport design. It also proved able to operate from the carrier *Kitty Hawk* without needing a catapult or arresting gear.

SPECIFICATIONS

CREW:	three
POWERPLANT:	four 33.4kN (7500lb-thrust) Lycoming YF102-LD-100 turbofan engines
MAX SPEED:	cruising speed 370km/h (230mph)
MAX ALTITUDE:	n/a
SPAN:	29.26m (96ft 0in)
LENGTH:	without probe 24.08m (79ft 0in)
HEIGHT:	8.71m (28ft 7in)
WEIGHT:	loaded 17,237kg (38,000lb)

The QSRA was used by NASA from 1978 to 1993. After the main STOL tests were completed, it was used to evaluate a 'jump strut' undercarriage to further shorten its take-off run.

The four engines exhausted over the top of the wing. The Coanda effect saw the airflow cling to the wing and flaps, generating propulsive lift.

The QSRA was later equipped with a digital fly-by-wire control system and head-up and head-down electronic displays. These allowed for very precise landings in particular, and contributed to the C-17 programme.

The Buffalo's two T64 turboprops were replaced by four Lycoming YF-102 turbofans, which had come from the two Northrop YA-9s, the unsuccessful competitor to the Republic A-10.

BOEING X-32 (2000)

The Joint Strike Fighter (JSF) programme aims to replace most of the F-16s, Harriers, F/A-18s and other aircraft in service with the US military and other air arms around the world. McDonnell Douglas, Boeing and Lockheed offered designs, with the former company being eliminated in late 1996. Boeing built the extraordinary X-32 to meet the requirements, which included development of a conventional USAF version, a STOVL model for the US Marine Corps and a carrier-capable naval version. The maiden flight of the conventional X-32A was on 18 September 2000, with Boeing test pilot Fred Knox at the controls. The X-32B STOVL demonstrator made its first hovering flight on 7 March 2001, and on 13 April 2001 the first airborne transition from conventional to STOVL mode and back again. The X-32 performed well, but was beaten to the lucrative JSF contract in October 2001.

SPECIFICATIONS (X-35A)

CREW:	one
POWERPLANT:	one 186.90kN (42,000lb-thrust) Pratt & Whitney F119-PW afterburning turbofan engine
MAX SPEED:	Mach 1.6
MAX ALTITUDE:	15,240m (50,000ft)
SPAN:	10.97m (36ft 0in)
LENGTH:	13.72m (45ft 0in)
HEIGHT:	4.06m (13ft 4in)
WEIGHT:	maximum 22,680kg (50,000lb)

The winner of the JSF 'fly-off' has the lion's share of the biggest defence programme in history. Unfortunately for Boeing and its startling-looking X-32, the loser is left with none of the spoils.

Unlike Lockheed, Boeing did not modify or build a version specifically to demonstrate its carrier capabilities, and the X-32A served as a demonstrator for both the USAF and USN mission.

X-32A

The X-32B's vertical thrust system is similar to that of the Harrier's, with vectoring nozzles under the wing around the centre of gravity. The main difference is the pitch-axis vectoring nozzle at the tail.

The huge intake in the nose attracted comments that the X-32 was too ugly to fly. Some hovering flights were made with the intake lip removed.

BOEING YC-14 *(1976)*

The US Air Force's AMST (Advanced Medium STOL Aircraft) programme was established to develop a jet replacement for the C-130 Hercules. Boeing's YC-14 used USB (upper surface blowing), where jet efflux was exhausted over the upper surface and adhered to the wing and flap surface, generating considerable extra lift. The first of the two YC-14s (72-1873 and 72-1874) took off on 9 August 1976, and it was flown for the US Air Force for a year before being returned to the manufacturer. Like the competing McDonnell Douglas YC-15, the YC-14 satisfied all the requirements of the AMST programme, but the money was not forthcoming for the next phase due to budget pressures. One YC-14 was stored and the other was displayed at Pima, Arizona.

SPECIFICATIONS

CREW:	three
POWERPLANT:	two 227kN (51,000lb-thrust) General Electric CF6-50D turbofans
MAX SPEED:	811km/h (504mph)
MAX ALTITUDE:	13,716m (45,000ft)
SPAN:	39.3m (129ft 0in)
LENGTH:	40.1m (131ft 8in)
HEIGHT:	14.7m (48ft 4in)
WEIGHT:	loaded 113,832kg (251,000lb)

Although the AMST programme failed to replace the Hercules, the overwing USB concept embodied in the YC-15 was used by Antonov for its An-72 and An-74 transports.

162

The supercritical wing was developed by NASA and provided highly efficient performance at high subsonic speeds. The flaps and USB (upper surface blowing) system gave especially good take-off performance.

The large flaps were of the Coanda type which causes airflow to stick to the convex side of an aerodynamic surface and generate extra lift.

The YC-14 had a capacity for 150 troops or 36,742kg (81,000lb) freight. When used from a short (572m/1875ft) field this reduced to 12,247kg (27,000lb).

163

CANADAIR CL-84 DYNAVERT (1965)

Canada's Dynavert was a private-venture attempt to create a tilt-wing tactical transport and gunship mainly for the export market.

The CL-84 began hovering trials on 7 May 1965 and was well advanced in its test programme when it crashed in September 1967. The crew escaped. Two improved CL-84-1s (military designation CX084) were ordered, and these were extensively tested from 1970, including firing trials with a minigun pod and use in a US/British/Canadian V/STOL instrumentation test programme. Landing trials were made on the USS *Guam* and *Guadalcanal* in 1973–74. The first CL-84-1 crashed at Patuxent River in July 1973. The Canadian military showed little interest in the concept and development ceased, but the trials contributed greatly to future craft such as the V-22. The third and only remaining Dynavert is an exhibit at the Canada Aviation Museum in Ottawa.

SPECIFICATIONS (CL-84-1)

CREW:	two
POWERPLANT:	two 1118kW (1500hp) Lycoming LTC1K-4A turboprop engines
MAX SPEED:	517km/h (321mph)
MAX ALTITUDE:	unknown
SPAN:	10.56m (34ft 8in)
LENGTH:	16.34m (53ft 8in)
HEIGHT:	(wing horizontal) 4.34m (14ft 3in)
WEIGHT:	maximum 6577kg (14,500lb)

The performance of helicopters greatly improved while the CL-84 was being perfected, spurred on by the Vietnam War. The Dynavert was a bit of a technical dead end, tilting rotors proving a better solution than tilting the whole wing.

The CL-84 had small rotors at the end of the fuselage to maintain pitch control in low-speed and hovering flight.

The CL-84's wing could be tilted beyond the vertical to 100 degrees, allowing backwards flight at up to 56km/h (35mph).

The tailplane and wing were interconnected up to 30 degrees of tilt, but beyond that the tailplane returned to the level position.

The original CL-84 had internal capacity for up to 12 troops in the main cabin. A payload of 1912kg (4215lb) could be carried in short take-off (STO) mode.

165

CONVAIR XFY-1 POGO (1954)

Convair's entry in the US Navy's competition for a VTOL interceptor was the XFY-1, usually known as the 'Pogo'. The Pogo's vertical and horizontal surfaces, which were almost the same size, each had a small castoring wheel at the tips, upon which the XFY-1 sat. In the event of an impending belly landing, the lower vertical fin could be jettisoned. Following a series of more than 250 tethered test flights inside an airship hangar, J.F. 'Skeets' Coleman made the first free flight in August 1954. This was a vertical flight, as the Pogo had no gear for a horizontal take-off or landing. The first transition to horizontal flight and back was made in November, and Coleman reported the Pogo was one of the best-handling aircraft he had flown (in conventional flight). The problem was backing the Pogo down accurately for a landing using throttle control alone.

SPECIFICATIONS

CREW:	one
POWERPLANT:	one 4362kW (5850hp) Allison XT40 turboprop engine
MAX SPEED:	982km/h (610mph)
MAX ALTITUDE:	unknown
WING SPAN:	8.43m (27ft 7in)
LENGTH:	10.66m (35ft 0in)
HEIGHT:	maximum 7371kg
WEIGHT:	(16,250lb)

Like the Lockheed 'Salmon', the Pogo was too demanding for a normal pilot to land safely in operational conditions. By the time techniques had been perfected and technical bugs worked out, the navy had lost interest in the concept.

The large spinner was intended to carry an air-to-air radar. Many point interceptors of the day were designed to work entirely under control of ground stations.

The pilot had the benefit of an ejector seat. This was arranged on a gimballed fitting so that it tilted 45 degrees forward for a more natural position during vertical operations.

NAVY

Development of the T40 engine was very protracted. When the XFV-1 and XFY-1 were nearing completion, only one example suitable for protracted hovering flight was available, and this was given to the Pogo.

CURTISS-WRIGHT X-19 *(1964)*

The Curtiss-Wright X-19 was a convertiplane which made use of the principle of radial lift, where specially designed propellers gave lift even when in horizontal mode, allowing for smaller wings. The private-venture twin-engined X-100 was flown in 1959 and won Bell a tri-service contract for a four-rotor X-19 test machine.

The X-19 was damaged attempting its first flight in November 1963 and did not start tethered trials until 26 June 1964. Work proceeded tentatively until 25 August 1965, when the number one aircraft was destroyed on its first full test flight, which was intended to demonstrate full transitions from vertical to horizontal flight and back. The two pilots made a lucky escape using their ejection seats while the X-19 was inverted at 122m (400ft). The second X-19 was never flown and wound up at the Aberdeen Proving Grounds. Its remains are being restored by the Martin Museum near Baltimore.

SPECIFICATIONS

CREW:	two
POWERPLANT:	two 1641kW (2200hp) Lycoming T55-L-5 turboshaft engines
MAX SPEED:	estimated 731km/h (454mph)
MAX ALTITUDE:	estimated 7803m (25,600ft)
SPAN:	6.55m (21ft 6in)
LENGTH:	13.53m (44ft 5in)
HEIGHT:	5.30m (17ft 5in)
WEIGHT:	loaded 6196kg (13,660lb)

The X-19 was not the most successful of X-planes. The crash of the only flying prototype essentially put an end to the concept of radial lift aircraft, other technologies proving more promising.

The horizontal or radial lift component was maximized by using short, wide propeller blades with exaggerated twist. They were largely made of foam plastic over a metal core.

The X-19's flight controls were conventional, with elevators and ailerons on the aft wing, and a rudder on the tailfin. The nacelle tilt was controlled by a switch on each control stick.

12197

TRI-SERVICE

X-19 VTOL

The X-19 was configured as a high-speed executive transport with six seats, although when ejection seats were added to the design the useful load dropped to almost nothing.

DORNIER DO 31 *(1967)*

The late 1950s saw the Luftwaffe attempt to create a largely VTOL force with fighters, attack aircraft and transports all able to operate after a Warsaw Pact strike on West Germany's bases. Many transport designs were proposed, but the Dornier Do 31 was the only one to reach the flight test stage. This had two Pegasus engines in underwing nacelles and wingtip pods with four smaller lift jets each. On 10 February 1967 the first Do 31 (the Do 31-E1) flew under Pegasus power alone, piloted by American Drury Wood. The -E3 followed in July with all 10 engines, and made full transition flights in December. NASA tested the Do 31 in Germany with a view to a potential Do 231 civil version, having up to 100 passengers, but military fashion had changed and in April 1970 the programme was cancelled. The Do 31-E1 is part of the Deutsches Museum collection in Munich.

SPECIFICATIONS (Do 31E-3)

CREW:	two
POWERPLANT:	two 68.95kN (15,500lb-thrust) Rolls-Royce Pegasus 5-2 vectored-thrust turbofans and eight 19.57kN (4,400lb-thrust) Rolls-Royce RB.162-4D turbojet engines
MAX SPEED:	cruising speed 644km/h (400mph)
MAX ALTITUDE:	10,515m (34,500ft)
SPAN:	18.06m (59ft 3in)
LENGTH:	20.88m (68ft 6in)
HEIGHT:	8.53m (28ft)
WEIGHT:	maximum 27,442kg (60,500lb)

The Do 31's 10-engine arrangement was an over-complex way to achieve VTOL, but could have been developed into a workable transport. By the time it was proving itself, the programme was cancelled.

During conventional flight the wingtip lift engines were redundant. One unusual aspect of flying the Do 31 was that the pilots had to remember to restart the lift engines before making the landing approach.

The two flying Do 31s, the -E1 and -E3 made a total of 149 test flights between them, but only the E3 was fitted for vertical flight. The Do 31-E2 was a non-flying static test example.

The Do 31 had a rear loading ramp for small vehicles or could seat up to 16 fully equipped troops.

DORNIER DO 29 (1958)

The 1950s and 1960s saw an explosion of research into vertical and short take-off and landing aircraft in Germany. Of the many propeller and jet driven designs of the period that used some sort of directed engine thrust, only a handful reached the hardware stage. The smallest and lightest was the Dornier Do 29, derived from the Do 27, a conventional STOL aircraft using high lift devices on the wings. The Do 29, which first flew in December 1958, replaced the Do 27's single nose-mounted engine with two pusher turboprops that could be tilted downwards as much as 90 degrees. With the engines angled at 70 degrees the Do 29 had a take-off run of 123m (405ft) and a landing run of 81m (265ft). With engines horizontal it had a stalling speed of 75km/h (47mph) and a minimum flying speed of 105km/h (65mph).

SPECIFICATIONS

CREW:	one
POWERPLANT:	two 201kW (270hp) Lycoming GO-480-B1A6 six-cylinder piston engines
MAX SPEED:	cruising speed 290km/h (180mph)
MAX ALTITUDE:	unknown
SPAN:	13.20m (43ft 4in)
LENGTH:	9.50m (31ft 2in)
HEIGHT:	unknown
WEIGHT:	maximum 2500kg (5511lb)

Like the other post-war German V/STOL designs, the 'tilt-engine' Dornier 29 had merit, but never entered service. The sole example is preserved at the Luftwaffen Museum at Gatow, near Berlin.

The wing retained the fixed slots and double slotted flaps of the Do 27, but had a new centre section which gave increased span and area.

The two Hartzell propellers turned in opposite directions to avoid torque effects. They were linked by a cross shaft to ensure they still turned in the event of one engine failing.

The pilot had a Martin Baker ejection seat and good visibility from the bubble canopy. A transparency in the forward fuselage allowed the pilot to see the landing spot during the approach.

EWR-SUD VJ 101C (1962)

In 1959 a consortium was formed by Bölkow, Heinkel and Messerschmitt to create a VTOL fighter (or VJ: Vertikal Jäger). All of these companies had been developing similar proposals and were encouraged to merge them into a sleek design with rotating wingtip engine pods. A bizarre ground rig called the Wippe (seesaw) was created to test the control system before the first flight article, the VJ 101C X1, intended to explore low-speed flight, made its first untethered flight in April 1963 in the hands of George Bright. The X1 reached Mach 1.08, then crashed in September 1964 due to a wrongly installed part, but the X2 with afterburners flew in June 1965, by which time the consortium had become a company called Entwicklungsring-Sud GmbH (EWR). The X2 was damaged in a hard landing in 1967, but was rebuilt. Although the proposed production version was cancelled, the X2 flew on until 1971, supporting the VAK 191 and Tornado programmes.

SPECIFICATIONS (X1)

CREW:	one
POWERPLANT:	six 12.23kN (2750lb-thrust) Rolls-Royce/MAN RB.145 non-afterburning turbojet engines
MAX SPEED:	1147km/h (713mph)
MAX ALTITUDE:	unknown
SPAN:	6.61m (21ft 8.25in)
LENGTH:	15.70m (51ft 6in)
HEIGHT:	4.13m (13ft 6.5in)
WEIGHT:	maximum 6000kg (13,228lb)

Sometimes called the Traumjäger (Dream Fighter), the sleek VJ 101 had certain problems, such as runway erosion from the engines in vertical mode. A production VJ 101D fighter version with a completely different engine arrangement was planned, but never built.

The VJ 101s had Martin Baker Mk 7 ejection seats. The successful use of the X1's seat prompted the Luftwaffe to fit Mk 7s in place of the Lockheed seats on its F-104G Starfighters.

The engines on the VJ 101C X2 had afterburners, boosting engine thrust to a maximum of 15.79kN (3350lb-thrust) each. The highest speed reached by the X2 was Mach 1.14.

The nacelles could be swivelled to six degrees forward of the vertical to allow braking and backwards flight. Each contained two RB.145 engines. There were two more mounted behind the cockpit.

FAIREY GYRODYNE (1947)

Two Gyrodynes were built as experimental machines, with the first flying on 7 December 1947. The Gyrodyne was a compound helicopter with wings and a tractor propeller on the starboard wingtip. This reduced the torque effect and the load on the main rotor, allowing higher cruising speeds. The engine and its complex system of gears and clutches amounted to half the empty weight of 1633kg (3600lb).

B.H. Arkell broke the straight-line rotorcraft speed record with a speed of 200.0065km/h (124.3mph) in June 1948. An attempt in 1949 to better the closed-circuit record ended in disaster when rotor head fatigue failure caused a crash. The second aircraft was rebuilt as the Jet Gyrodyne with a new, larger two-bladed rotor with tip jets, pusher propellers and a new transmission. The engine was barely adequate to lift the aircraft and power the burners for transition to horizontal flight, but this was successfully achieved more than 200 times by 1956.

SPECIFICATIONS (Gyrodyne)

CREW:	two
POWERPLANT:	one 392kW (525hp) Alvis Leonides nine cylinder radial
MAX SPEED:	225km/h (140mph)
MAX ALTITUDE:	3048m (10,000ft)
LENGTH:	7.62m (25ft)
ROTOR DIAMETER:	(51ft 8in)
HEIGHT:	3.10m (10ft 2in)
WEIGHT:	loaded 2177kg (4800lb)

The Gyrodyne and then the Jet Gyrodyne contributed to the much larger turbine-powered Rotodyne airliner of the same configuration. The Gyrodyne is preserved at the Museum of Berkshire Aviation in Woodley, Berkshire.

The Gyrodyne had a three blade main rotor driven by a conventional crankshaft. The Jet Gyrodyne had two very long blades, driven by compressed air expelled by the Fairey pressure jets at the rotor tips.

The Jet Gyrodyne's wing propellers used differential variable pitch to give directional control. Tip jets powered the rotors, but the main power source was still a piston engine.

The cockpit seated two, and there was room for three passengers sitting on a bench seat in the rear of the cabin. The main structure was based around a steel tube frame.

HAWKER P.1127 *(1960)*

After many false starts, a practical VTOL combat aircraft had its origin in 1960 when the theories of Frenchman Marcel Wibault, the new Bristol BS.53 vectoring thrust engine and the design expertise of Hawker Aircraft came together in the P.1127, progenitor of the Harrier. Bill Bedford began hovering trials with the first P.1127 (XP831) on 21 October 1960. Two prototypes were followed by a development batch of four aircraft, the last of which flew in February 1964. The P.1127s flew until 1975, establishing the flight and operating characteristics from sea and land for vectored thrust VTOL. The success of the P.1127 led to the similar XV-6A Kestrel, which was evaluated by UK, USAF, US Army and German pilots, and which begat the operational Harrier GR.1 and AV-8A.

SPECIFICATIONS

CREW:	one
POWERPLANT:	one 48.93kN (11,000lb-thrust) Bristol Siddeley Pegasus 3 vectoring thrust turbofan
MAX SPEED:	1207km/h (720mph)
MAX ALTITUDE:	15,179m (49,800ft)
SPAN:	7.42m (24ft 4in)
LENGTH:	including probe 14.93m (49ft 0in)
HEIGHT:	3.28m (10ft 9in)
WEIGHT:	loaded 7031kg (15,500lb)

The P.1127 was simple in comparison with its competitors and was the first really practical VTOL combat aircraft. It was the predecessor of the Harrier and its derivatives, and the ancestor of the F-35 Joint Strike Fighter.

Intake lips that inflated for greater airflow when hovering and deflated for high-speed flight were tried, but tended to rip and were replaced on the Harrier by auxiliary intake doors.

The early Pegasus engines gave only marginally more thrust than the weight of the P.1127. All surplus equipment was left off and minimal fuel carried to give reasonable hovering performance.

The first P.1127 is preserved at London's Science Museum. Others are displayed at Yeovilton in Somerset and at the Brooklands Museum in Surrey.

The P.1127's four-poster exhaust layout allowed a single engine to provide thrust and lift without the dead weight of lift engines and other contrivances.

HILLER X-18 *(1959)*

The X-18 was the first tilt-wing aircraft to fly and the first large VTOL aircraft produced in the USA. Designed to test the suitability of a tilt-wing for future civil aircraft applications, the only prototype made its first flights in November 1959 with George Bright and Bruce Jones at the controls. During its short flight career, the X-18 never demonstrated a full transition from vertical and horizontal flight and back again, only ever reaching a 35-degree wing angle. In November 1960, after 20 flights, a propeller governor failed and the X-18 only just avoided a crash. After that it was grounded and used only for static tests. When these were over in January 1964 the X-18 was scrapped at Edwards Air Force Base, California.

SPECIFICATIONS

CREW:	two
POWERPLANT:	two 4364kW (5850hp) Allison YT40-A-14 turboprop engines, and one 15.12kN (3400lb-thrust) Westinghouse J34-WE-36 turbojet engine for pitch control
MAX SPEED:	407km/h (253mph)
MAX ALTITUDE:	11,064m (36,300ft)
SPAN:	14.6m (48ft 0in)
LENGTH:	without boom (63ft 0in)
HEIGHT:	7.50m (24ft 7in)
WEIGHT:	loaded 14,969kg (33,000lb)

The X-18 did not achieve a great deal in its limited flying career. Its engines were not cross-shafted, giving no back-up in case of a failure. Nevertheless, it was the ancestor of several important V/STOL programmes.

The wings could rotate to a 90-degree angle for vertical flight. A curved line on the fuselage allowed observers to judge the degree of rotation.

The fuselage of the X-18 had once belonged to a Chase YC-122C transport aircraft and the engines had been previously used in the Convair XFY-1 and Lockheed XFV-1 tail-sitter VTOL aircraft.

A Westinghouse J34 engine was installed in the rear fuselage solely to provide control in the pitch axis during hovering and transitional flight.

HUNTING H.126 (1963)

The Hunting 126 was developed for the UK's National Gas Turbine Establishment to explore the idea of using engine exhaust gases as a 'jet flap' to eliminate the structural weight of physical flaps and their components. On 26 March 1963 XN714 flew for the first time and went on to make more than 100 flights. Unfortunately the piping, ducting and heat shielding needed to move the hot air from the engine to the wing weighed at least as much as conventional flaps, and the jet flap idea was shelved. In 1969 XN714 as sent to the USA for tests inside a large NASA wind tunnel. When it returned it was never reassembled and eventually found its way into the RAF Museum collection. It is now displayed at Cosford. The second prototype, XN719, was never completed and eventually scrapped.

SPECIFICATIONS

CREW:	one
POWERPLANT:	one 21.57kN (4850lb-thrust) Bristol Siddeley Orpheus 805 turbojet
MAX SPEED:	engine
MAX ALTITUDE:	unknown
SPAN:	unknown
LENGTH:	13.83m (45ft 4in) without probe 13.54m
HEIGHT:	(44ft 3in)
WEIGHT:	4.72m (15ft 6in) unknown

The remarkably ugly Hunting 126 was built to explore high-lift flight through diversion of engine thrust to the high-lift wing. The USA showed an interest in the concept, but it proved too cumbersome for further development.

Gases bled off the engine were blown as a sheet over the wing when vertical lift was needed. Puffer jets in the wings, rear fuselage and tailcone aided roll, yaw and pitch control at low speeds.

The ungainly 126 was painted yellow overall and had a characteristic nose-down flying attitude, making it one of the most distinctive aircraft in British skies during its test programme.

The gas lift system allowed for a small narrow-chord wing. Any weight and drag advantages this had were lost by the bracing strut, fixed undercarriage and complex propulsion system.

LOCKHEED MARTIN X-35 JSF (2000)

Lockheed's contender in the Joint Strike Fighter competition was the X-35, designed in three versions to meet the needs of the US Air Force, Navy and Marine Corps. Unlike Boeing's 'whale-mouthed' X-32, it had side-mounted intakes optimized for low radar visibility. Tom Morgenfeld made the first flight in the X-35A on 24 October 2000. The X-35C flew on 16 December that year. After 27 test flights, the X-35A was rebuilt as the X-35B, which uses a shaft-driven lift fan to allow vertical take-offs and landings. It flew in this form in June 2001. The US Navy's carrier-capable X-35C flew in February 2001. This was strengthened and fitted with a larger wing and arresting hook. The X-35 was chosen as the JSF winner in October 2001. Development under the designation F-35 (it should logically be F-24) is under way, with potential production of up to 6000 aircraft. The production F-35 will have a new engine and bear only a superficial resemblance to the X-35. Both the X-35s have been preserved for museum display.

SPECIFICATIONS

CREW:	one
POWERPLANT:	one 187kN (42,000lb-thrust) Pratt & Whitney F119-PW-611C afterburning turbofan engine
MAX SPEED:	Mach 1.8
MAX ALTITUDE:	13,716m (45,000ft)
SPAN:	13.12m (43ft)
LENGTH:	15.52m (50ft 11in)
HEIGHT:	4.60m (15ft 2in)
WEIGHT:	loaded 17,485kg (38,549lb)

Compared with the Boeing X-32, Lockheed's X-35 is almost boringly conventional in appearance, being not unlike a scaled-down F/A-22 Raptor in some respects. Many details of the production F-35 have yet to be finalized.

The X-35A, B and C were actually only two aircraft. The X-35B STO/VL variant was converted from the conventional take-off and landing X-35A.

The X-35 contained many components from other aircraft. The main landing gear came from the A-6 Intruder. Other parts were from the F-15E Eagle, the F/A-18E/F, the YF-23, the F/A-22, the B-2, AV-8B, the C-130J Hercules and the F-16.

The X-35B has a main nozzle that bends to direct the thrust downwards for vertical take-off and landing. This is the most complex part of the whole aircraft.

LOCKHEED XFV-1 SALMON (1954)

The XFV-1 was the first of the two turboprop-powered 'tail-sitters' to be built to a 1950 US Navy requirement for a point-defence interceptor. In March 1954, Herman 'Fish' Salmon took the XFV-1 on its first flight. He was to be the sole pilot for the project, and the aircraft received the unofficial name 'Salmon'. All its take-offs were made in horizontal mode using a cumbersome fixed undercarriage arrangement. The YT40 turboprop was not considered reliable enough to bear the sole responsibility for keeping the aircraft aloft through a full vertical-horizontal-vertical translation from take-off to landing. In all 32 test flights were made and transitions to and from the vertical position were made a number of times, but the idea was shown to be impractical and the programmed was cancelled in 1955.

SPECIFICATIONS

CREW:	one
POWERPLANT:	one 4362kW (5850hp) Allison YT40-A-6 turboprop engine
MAX SPEED:	estimated 933km/h (580mph)
MAX ALTITUDE:	unknown
SPAN:	8.35m (27ft 5in)
LENGTH:	11.43m (37ft 6in)
HEIGHT:	unknown
WEIGHT:	maximum 7358kg (16,221lb)

The remarkable XFV-1 offered the prospect of a fighter on every warship, but was impractical for operation other than in daylight and good weather, and needed an exceptional pilot at the controls.

The massive contra-rotating propellers had a diameter of 4.88m (16ft 0in). A contraprop layout eliminated the torque effect that would otherwise have seen the airframe twist around the propellers.

Controlling the descent and ascent required the pilot to carefully adjust the throttle, taking account of a lag between making the adjustment and its effect being felt.

The sole XFV-1 has passed through several museum collections. It is believed to be currently at the EAA's Sport Aviation Museum at Lakeland, Florida.

LOCKHEED XV-4 HUMMINGBIRD (1962)

The result of a US Army requirement for a battlefield surveillance and target acquisition platform, the XV-4 was begun under the designation VZ-10. The first prototype's initial conventional flight was made on 7 July 1962, and began hovering trials in May 1963. The first transition from vertical to horizontal flight occurred in November 1963. Unfortunately it suffered a fatal accident in June 1964. The surviving aircraft was rebuilt as the XV-4A Hummingbird II with lift-jets, and flew as such in January 1969, but crashed in March. In a few years technology had advanced to where small lightweight lift-jets offered more thrust per pound than did lift fans, and the US Air Force was wary of the US Army getting into the jet business. A new version called the XV-4B was ordered, but never built.

SPECIFICATIONS

CREW:	one
POWERPLANT:	two 14.68kN (3300lb-thrust) Pratt & Whitney JT12A turbojet engines
MAX SPEED:	540km/h (336mph)
MAX ALTITUDE:	12,400m (40,684ft)
SPAN:	7.9m (26ft)
LENGTH:	10.30m (32ft)
HEIGHT:	3.58m (11ft 8in)
WEIGHT:	loaded 5265kg (11,607lb)

The somewhat unlucky Hummingbird was another unsuccessful attempt to introduce jets to the US Army. Its VTOL system was too cumbersome and failed to perform to expectations.

The XV-4's thrust augmentation proved less effective than predicted in the lab, giving only about a 4 per cent excess of thrust over weight. This type of result illustrates the worth of having a flying testbed.

The jet thrust was diverted into augmentor ejectors for vertical take-off and landing. These were cross-linked so as to provide balanced thrust in the event of engine failure.

The vertical lift system was constructed largely of stainless steel and titanium, and these heavy components made up a large proportion of the Hummingbird's empty weight.

CHANCE-VOUGHT/LTV XC-142A (1964)

The XC-142A was designed as a vertical/short take-off and landing (V/STOL) transport, able to carry 32 troops at a high cruising speed to the battlefield. Five were built for evaluation by the US Army, Navy and Air Force, and the first flew on 29 September 1964.

These five examples flew nearly 500 times between 1964 and 1967, and proved capable of flying at up to 694km/h (431mph) forwards and 56km/h (35mph) backwards, and operating from very rough and short airstrips. Freight and paratroop dropping was demonstrated, and one XC-142A was operated from the aircraft carrier USS *Bennington*. In May 1967 one of the XC-142As crashed, killing the three test crew.

Only one of the five aircraft remains, having made its last flight to the USAF Museum in Dayton, Ohio, in 1970.

SPECIFICATIONS

CREW:	three
POWERPLANT:	four 13.70kN (3080lb-thrust) General Electric T64-GE-1 turboprop engines
MAX SPEED:	694km/h (431mph)
MAX ALTITUDE:	694km/h (431mph)
SPAN:	7620m (25,000ft)
LENGTH:	20.57m (67ft 6in)
HEIGHT:	17.71m (58ft 2in)
WEIGHT:	7.82m (25ft 8in) maximum 18,824kg (41,500lb)

The XC-142A was the world's first successful V/STOL transport aircraft. Its tilt-wing design allowed for either short or vertical take-offs and landings.

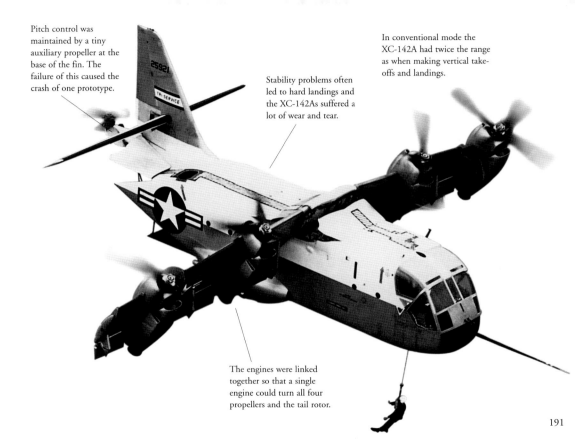

Pitch control was maintained by a tiny auxiliary propeller at the base of the fin. The failure of this caused the crash of one prototype.

Stability problems often led to hard landings and the XC-142As suffered a lot of wear and tear.

In conventional mode the XC-142A had twice the range as when making vertical take-offs and landings.

The engines were linked together so that a single engine could turn all four propellers and the tail rotor.

MCDONNELL DOUGLAS YC-15 (1975)

McDonnell competed for the AMST demonstrator contract with its four-engined YC-15. Generally similar in configuration to Boeing's YC-14, the YC-15 achieved its STOL performance by directing its thrust towards its double-slotted flaps. Some of the air pushed against the flaps' underside, and the rest went through and over the top surface due to the Coanda effect. A 600-hour flight test programme began on 26 August 1975.

Due to budget difficulties, the AMST project was cancelled in 1979, and a new effort dubbed 'CX' (cargo experimental) began. This eventually led to the McDonnell Douglas C-17, which owed a lot to the YC-15. The second aircraft (72-1876) was preserved at Pima, Arizona, and the aircraft 72-1875 was stored. In 1996 this second aircraft was returned to flight in support of C-17 development efforts.

SPECIFICATIONS
(first aircraft 72-1875)

CREW:	three
POWERPLANT:	four 71kN (16,000lb-thrust) Pratt & Whitney JT8D-17 turbofan engines
MAX SPEED:	805km/h (500mph)
MAX ALTITUDE:	9144m (30,000ft)
SPAN:	40.42m (132ft 7in)
LENGTH:	37.86m (124 ft 3in)
HEIGHT:	13.18m (43ft 4in)
WEIGHT:	99,418kg (219,180lb)

The YC-15 was a successful response to the USAF's STOL transport requirement, even though it was not chosen for production. It had a significant influence on the McDonnell Douglas (now Boeing) C-17 Globemaster III.

The two YC-15s had different wingspans. The first aircraft's wings were longer at 40.42m (132ft 7in) than the second's at 33.6m (110ft 4in).

After 15 years of storage one YC-15 was reactivated as an Advanced Technology Demonstrator (ATD), which helped to speed up development of the C-17 by test flying new equipment.

The YC-15's four underslung engines produced less thrust than the YC-14's two large engines and gave a lower performance, although this was not important in the context of the demonstration programme.

F-15 SMTD/ACTIVE (1988)

In an effort to reduce runway distances and improve combat agility, the first two-seat F-15B Eagle (72-091) was modified under the Short takeoff and landing/Maneuverability Technology Demonstrator (SMTD) programme. Large movable canard foreplanes were fitted, as (after 43 flights) were two-dimensional (up and down movement only) thrust-vectoring engine nozzles. The first flight, with pilot Larry Walker at the controls, was made on 7 September 1988. The F-15 SMTD made 138 flights up to August 1991. The Eagle was then modified under a NASA/USAF programme as the F-15B ACTIVE (Advanced Control Technology for Integrated Vehicles), with new thrust-vectoring nozzles that could turn 20 degrees in any direction, and it flew again as such in February 1996. The F-15B achieved thrust vectoring at speeds of up to Mach 1.95 by the end of the year.

SPECIFICATIONS

CREW:	two
POWERPLANT:	two 129.0kN (29,000lb-thrust) Pratt & Whitney F100-PW-229 thrust-vectoring afterburning turbofans
MAX SPEED:	Mach 2.0
MAX ALTITUDE:	18,280m (60,000ft)
SPAN:	13.05m (42ft 10in)
LENGTH:	19.41m (63ft 8in)
HEIGHT:	5.63m (18ft 6in)
WEIGHT:	21,319kg (47,000lb)

The F-15 SMTD/ACTIVE demonstrated the utility of thrust vectoring control (TVC) on a twin-engined fighter. It was not adopted for any production F-15, but TVC is an integral part of the F/A-22 Raptor.

The canard foreplanes were modified F/A-18 Hornet tailplanes, mounted at a 20-degree dihedral (downward angle). They could be operated either symmetrically or differentially.

For rough field landings the STMD F-15 had a strengthened undercarriage. An additional ground mapping mode was added to the radar to help the pilot find an improvised airstrip from a distance.

The F-15B ACTIVE was used to explore the use of thrust vectoring as a means of control at high speeds and even as a replacement for vertical tailfins. A planned follow-on programme with tails removed did not take place.

MCDONNELL XV-1 *(1954)*

McDonnell's unusual machine was first designated L-25 (for Liaison), then H-35 in the helicopter series. It later became the XV-1 in the new V-for-Vertical category, which covered all VTOL aircraft other than conventional helicopters by the time it first flew free on 11 February 1954. The second prototype was damaged soon after its first flight in June 1954, and it was not until April 1955 that an XV-1 made a transition to horizontal flight. In October 1956 one XV-1 aircraft exceeded 322km/h (200mph), the first rotorcraft to do so.

With conventional helicopters achieving higher and higher performance without the burden of complicated propulsion systems such as that on the XV-1, the programme was abandoned in 1957. The XV-1s were retired and are now part of the US Army and National Air and Space collections.

SPECIFICATIONS

CREW:	two
POWERPLANT:	one 410kW (550hp) Continental R-975-19 7-cylinder radial piston engine
MAX SPEED:	327km/h (203mph)
MAX ALTITUDE:	unknown
SPAN:	7.92m (26ft 0in)
LENGTH:	15.24m (50ft 0in)
HEIGHT:	3.05m (10ft 0in)
WEIGHT:	loaded 2495kg (5500lb)

One of the only twin-boomed rotorcraft, the tandem-cockpit XV-1 was more gyroplane than helicopter. Without its rotors it was an unusual twin-boomed aeroplane with a pusher propeller.

After take-off the single engine was switched from driving the rotors through the tip jets to running the pusher propeller. The main rotor was then left to freewheel and contribute to lift.

The slightly swept wings had a span of 7.9m (25ft 11in) and mounted conventional ailerons with prominent mass balances.

The radial engine drove the pusher propeller at the rear of the fuselage for forward flight or was used to compress air that was mixed with fuel and ignited in the tip jets to power the rotors directly.

MIKOYAN-GUREVICH MIG-23PD 'FAITHLESS' (1967)

The MiG-23PD followed the largely unsuccessful MiG-21PD of 1966. With only two RD-36-35 lift engines, the MiG-21PD could not achieve a true vertical take-off or landing. It also had poor handling at low speed. The development of the Tumanskii R-27 engine allowed MiG to develop a new tactical fighter to replace the MiG-21. The Kremlin directed that the first R-27-equipped MiG should also have a bay for two lift engines. The MiG 23-01 or MiG-23PD first flew with Pyotr Ostapenko on 3 April 1967. Like the MiG-21PD, it could not operate vertically and stayed above 150km/h (93mph) during flight. At the same time Mikoyan was tasked with developing a variable geometry ('swing-wing') version of the same basic design. This was designated the 23-11m or MiG-23S, and went on to become a successful family of interceptors and ground-attack aircraft.

SPECIFICATIONS

CREW:	one
POWERPLANT:	one 76.5kN (17,196lb-thrust) Tumanskii R-27-300 afterburning turbofan and two 23.0kN (5181lb-thrust) Koliesov RD-36-35 lift jets
MAX SPEED:	unknown
MAX ALTITUDE:	unknown
SPAN:	7.72m (25ft 4in)
LENGTH:	excluding boom 16.8m (55ft 2in)
HEIGHT:	5.15m (16ft 8in)
WEIGHT:	loaded 16,000kg (35,273lb)

The MiG-23 had only a brief career, as variable geometry wings offered better take-off and landing characteristics than did marrying a delta wing with extra lift engines.

The 23-01 was displayed at the 1967 Moscow air show with a dummy gun, two types of missiles and a large tactical number painted on the nose. These measures aimed to convince Western observers that the MiG-23PD was in or nearing service.

The thrust of the lift jets was only about a quarter of the empty weight of the 23-01, ruling out VTOL operations. Use of the jets gave a take-off run of 180–200m (591–656ft) in a lightly loaded condition.

Although in profile the MiG-23PD resembled the MiG-23S 'Flogger', the latter's intake system variable ramps was quite different and allowed much higher maximum speeds.

MIL V-12 HOMER (1968)

The USSR's premier helicopter design bureau, Mil was tasked with creating a rotary-wing equivalent of the Antonov AN-22 transport aircraft, able to carry the same loads, such as ballistic missiles and mobile launchers, but to deliver them directly to remote sites. In order to give an unencumbered cabin, the design team chose a layout used on few helicopters, with the rotors in a side-by-side layout on long booms. Known as the V-12 in the USSR and as the Mi-12 with the reporting name 'Homer' in the West, the giant helicopter's first flight was in 1968. During 1969 the V-12 set seven load-carrying records. These included a lift of 31,030kg (68,409lb) to 2951m (9683ft) and later 40,204kg (88,635lb) to 2255m (7400ft). Although three prototypes were built and they made appearances in the West, development was abandoned in favour of the single-rotor Mi-26 'Halo', which first appeared in 1977 and took the crown of 'world's largest helicopter'.

SPECIFICATIONS

CREW:	six
POWERPLANT:	four 4849kW (6500hp) Soloviev D-25VF turboshaft engines
MAX SPEED:	259km/h (161mph)
MAX ALTITUDE:	3500m (11,500ft)
ROTOR DIAMETER:	35.0m (114ft 10in)
LENGTH:	37.0m (121ft 5in)
HEIGHT:	12.5m (41ft 0in)
WEIGHT:	maximum 105,000kg (231,485lb)

The V-12 was impressive, but complicated and cumbersome. Advances in turboshaft engine technology allowed the next generation of heavylift Russian helicopters to have a conventional layout.

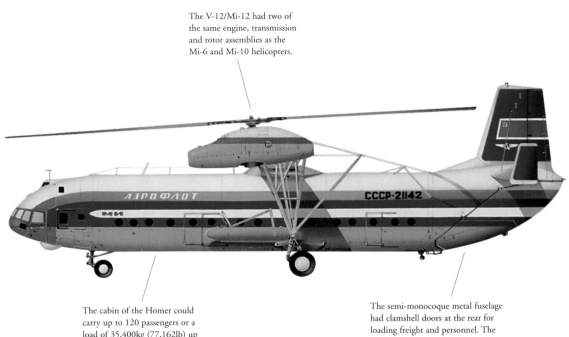

The V-12/Mi-12 had two of the same engine, transmission and rotor assemblies as the Mi-6 and Mi-10 helicopters.

The cabin of the Homer could carry up to 120 passengers or a load of 35,400kg (77,162lb) up to a range of 500km (311 miles).

The semi-monocoque metal fuselage had clamshell doors at the rear for loading freight and personnel. The cockpit was mounted above the front part of the cabin.

PESCARA NO. 3 HELICOPTER (1923)

Spaniard Raul Pateras Pescara (who was also known as the Marquis de Pescara) built his first unsuccessful co-axial rotor helicopter in 1922. He returned to the drawing board, and his No. 2 machine achieved limited flight in Spain and was tested in France by the military. The No. 3 machine, built in France in 1923, was much more successful. Flights of up to 10 minutes' duration were possible, as was low-speed forward motion. On 18 April 1924 Pescara flew the No. 3 at Issy-les-Moulineaux over a distance of 736m (2415ft) in a flight that took over four minutes and broke a newly established helicopter distance record. A version called the No. 3F may have been rebuilt from the No. 3 and fitted with a 187kW (250hp) engine. It used an additional propeller for cooling purposes. Trials in 1925 showed it to be little improvement over the No. 3 and Pescara gave up helicopter work and returned to Spain.

SPECIFICATIONS

CREW:	one
POWERPLANT:	one 134kW (180hp) Hispano-Suiza V-type piston engine
MAX SPEED:	approx 13km/h (8mph)
MAX ALTITUDE:	unknown
ROTOR DIAMETER:	7.20m (23ft 8in)
HEIGHT:	unknown
WEIGHT:	empty 850kg (1874lb)

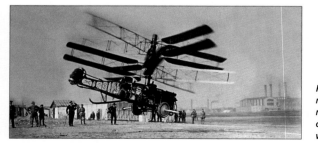

Pescara combined such features as a tilting rotorhead for forward motion and a coaxial rotor system to eliminate torque. Despite its comical appearance, his No. 3 helicopter was ahead of its time.

Unlike most earlier and contemporary helicopters, the No. 3 did not have a separate engine and propeller for forward propulsion. Tilting the rotorhead and warping some of the rotorblades provided forward thrust.

The Pescara No. 3 had no fewer than 16 lifting surfaces and was essentially a collection of biplane wings mounted on an axle. A boom structure in the forward part balanced the pilot, who sat behind the engine.

Like many helicopter pioneers, Pescara conducted some of his early flight trials inside a large building to eliminate the influence of gusts and breezes.

ROCKWELL XFV-12A *(1972)*

Technological and budgetary problems caused a series of delays to the XFV-12A programme, and it eventually faded away in the late 1970s. Designed to fly from small aircraft-carriers without catapults or arresting gear, the XFV-12A presented complex engineering problems that could not be solved within the restricted budget available, even though the concept of diverting engine thrust to provide jet-lift for take-off and landing seemed practical in theory. Unfortunately, the XFV-12A only ever left the ground while suspended under the NASA Lunar Lander gantry in Virginia. A special rig which rotated at high speed was built to test the Pratt & Whitney F401-PW-400 turbofan and its associated thrust diverter valve. The engine produced thrust that was ducted to a complete wing assembly set on a long arm. Rig tests did not lead to a flight, however, and the US Navy eventually stated that it had 'learned all it could' from the Rockwell XFV-12A.

SPECIFICATIONS

CREW:	one
POWERPLANT:	one 133.40kN (30,000lb-thrust) Pratt & Whitney F401-PW-400 turbofan engine
MAX SPEED:	projected Mach 2.2–2.4
WING SPAN:	8.69m (28ft 6in)
LENGTH:	13.39m (43ft 11in)
HEIGHT:	3.5m (10ft 4in)
WEIGHT:	6259kg (3890lb)

Known by the US Navy designation, NR-356, this artist's impression shows the XFV-12A as it might have appeared in service, with modified wings and vertical tail surfaces. The aircraft would have been hugely expensive.

A long nose radome disguised the fact that the forward fuselage and cockpit area were from the Skyhawk. The pilot sat on a McDonnell Douglas Escapac zero-zero ejection seat in a pressurised and air-conditioned cockpit. No radar was fitted.

The Skyhawk undercarriage of the XFV-12A was fully retractable, with the main units retracting backwards into wingtip fairings and the nose gear retracting forwards.

Fixed to each wingtip was an endplate, which formed the vertical stabilising surfaces of the aircraft during flight. The upper section incorporated a fixed fin and rudder, the lower only a fin. Each wing had full-span trailing-edge flaps.

SCALED COMPOSITES SPACESHIPONE (2003)

B urt Rutan's most ambitious design yet, the SpaceShipOne was created to compete for the Ansari X-Prize, a competition to fly a three-person craft above 100km (62 miles) altitude, regarded as the limit of the earth's atmosphere. Brian Binnie made its first powered test flight on 17 December 2003, the 100th anniversary of the Wright Brothers' first flights at Kitty Hawk. Mike Melvill piloted the first privately financed space flight on 21 June 2004, and again exceeded 100km on 29 September. On 4 October SpaceShipOne made a second sub-orbital flight within two weeks, this time to 112km (367,442ft) or 69.6 miles above the earth, and captured the $10 million Ansari X-Prize.

Together with Richard Branson's new company Virgin Galactic, Scaled Composites plans to develop a seven-seat 'SpaceShipTwo' to offer commercial flights into space.

SPECIFICATIONS

CREW:	one
POWERPLANT:	one 74kN (16,535lb-thrust) SpaceDev hybrid solid rocket engine
MAX SPEED:	Mach 3.09 (3518 km/h)
MAX ALTITUDE:	111,996m (367,442ft)
SPAN:	4.99m (16ft 4in)
LENGTH:	5.00m (16ft 5in)
HEIGHT:	unknown
WEIGHT:	loaded 3600kg (7937lb)

SpaceShipOne is the first privately designed and owned sub-orbital vehicle. With its White Knight mothership it is one of the most unusual aircraft ever flown and may be the progenitor of a whole family of spacecraft.

The registration letters N328KF were chosen to signify 328,000ft. The preferred registration N100KM (100km) was already taken.

The SpaceShipOne is powered by a solid fuel rocket motor, which burns a mix of nitrous oxide (laughing gas) and hydroxy-terminated polybutadiene or tyre rubber.

When the engine burns out the occupants of SpaceShipOne experience zero gravity for several minutes. On the X-Prize flights only weights representing passengers were carried.

SpaceShipOne is lifted to launch attitude of 15,240m (50,000ft) by a carrier plane called the White Knight. After release SpaceShipOne's own rocket fires for up to 80 seconds to propel it out of the atmosphere.

RYAN XV-5 VERTIFAN *(1964)*

The XV-5 was developed for the US Army as a potential battlefield surveillance platform. General Electric was responsible for the power system that used two engines driving three fans to provide lift and pitch control. The first flight was made in May 1964, and the first vertical flight was achieved in July, but the prototype was destroyed in a 1965 accident. In October 1966 a trial with a sling load went wrong and the second XV-5 rolled violently. The pilot ejected, but sadly he was killed. The XV-5 was recovered and was not badly damaged when it crash-landed. It was rebuilt for further testing. The Army's test programme encompassed 338 flights up to March 1967, when the surviving XV-5 was passed to NASA at the Ames Research Center and modified into the XV-5B with the undercarriage moved outboard of the wing fans. This gave better ground stability and braking. As the XV-5B it continued V/STOL research until 1974 and is preserved today at the Army Aviation Museum at Fort Rucker, Alabama.

SPECIFICATIONS

CREW:	one
POWERPLANT:	two 11.79kN (2650lb-thrust) General Electric J85-GE-5 turbojet engines
MAX SPEED:	804km/h (498mph)
MAX ALTITUDE:	12,200m (40,028ft)
SPAN:	9.09m (29ft 10in)
LENGTH:	13.56m (44ft 6in)
HEIGHT:	4.50m (14ft 9in)
WEIGHT:	loaded 5580kg (12,302lb)

The XV-5 was quite a good design which was hampered by the weight and volume required for its lift fans. The basic fan design had originated with the Avro VZ-9 'flying saucer' of 1959.

The XV-5 had a fan in each wing for vertical lift and a smaller fan in the nose for additional lift and for pitch control. The fans were powered by the exhaust gases of the two engines that also gave forward thrust.

Sustained hovering flight in the Vertifan was said to be easier than in a helicopter. Roll control in vertical and hovering flight was effected by applying differential power to the wing fans.

The J85 turbojets were cross-connected so that either could drive all three lift fans in the event of a failure, although the power would be reduced.

U.S. ARMY
24506

SAUNDERS-ROE SR.53 (1957)

A 1952 specification for a high-performance interceptor was met by flying-boat builder Saunders-Roe (Saro) with the mixed-powerplant SR.53. The main jet engine was of low power, but the fully variable Spectre rocket motor allowed the SR.53 to climb to 18,288m (60,000ft) in 3.3 minutes from brake release. XD145, the first SR.53, made its debut flight on 16 May 1957, piloted by John Booth. XD151 flew in December. The SR.53's tiny nose only had room for a small gun ranging radar and an operational SR.53 would have relied entirely on ground control to make an interception. The need for a radar-equipped interceptor with greater endurance (which would have been the SR.177) saw the SR.53 relegated to a high-speed missile test platform. The loss of XD151 and John Booth in an accident in March 1958 saw the effective end of the SR.53. The SR.177 was axed in the infamous 1957 Defence Review.

SPECIFICATIONS

CREW:	one
POWERPLANT:	one 7.30kN (1640lb-thrust) Armstrong Siddeley A.S.V.8 Viper 101 turbojet and one 31.14kN (7000lb-thrust) de Havilland Spectre 1A rocket engine
MAX SPEED:	Mach 2.1
MAX ALTITUDE:	(projected) 39,000m (130,000ft)
SPAN:	7.64m (25ft 1in)
LENGTH:	14.14m (46ft 5in)
HEIGHT:	3.31m (10ft 10in)
WEIGHT:	loaded 8346kg (18,400lb)

The SR.53 was a high performance machine, but as an operational fighter it would have had many drawbacks. The surviving prototype XD145 is displayed at the RAF Museum's Cosford facility.

The airbrakes proved too effective in their original form, so were perforated to let some of the airflow pass through.

The SR.53 was one of the first aircraft to carry missiles on wingtip rails. During tests a camera and instrumentation pod was sometimes mounted opposite a Firestreak AAM.

The Viper turbojet was mounted above the Spectre rocket, which used hydrogen peroxide (HTP) fuel. The rocket fuel would have presented considerable handling difficulties at squadron level.

SHORT SC.1 *(1957)*

I ntended as a pure research aircraft to explore low-speed VTOL flight, the
Short SC.1 made use of the newly developed RB.108 lift engine for both
lift and propulsion. It was built as a compact, lightweight airframe to allow
as much thrust for vertical lift.

On 2 April 1957 Tom Brooke-Smith made the first (conventional)
flight of XG900, the first of two SC.1s ordered in 1954. The second aircraft
(XG905) began tethered hovering trials in May 1958, followed later by
untethered flights and an appearance at the 1960 Farnborough Air Show
where the intake ingested mown grass, cutting the display short. One
achievement of the SC.1s was to develop the rolling take-off technique which
was later used by the Harrier.

XG905 crashed due to gyro failure in October 1963, killing the pilot. The
airframe was repairable and continued flying on blind landing trials along
with XG900 until 1967.

SPECIFICATIONS

CREW:	one
POWERPLANT:	five 9.58kN (2130lb-thrust) Rolls-Royce RB.108
MAX SPEED:	413km/h (257mph)
MAX ALTITUDE:	
SPAN:	7.16m (23ft 6in)
LENGTH:	9.14m (30ft 0in)
HEIGHT:	3.25m (10ft 8in)
WEIGHT:	loaded 3493kg (7700lb)

*The SC.1 was never intended to form the basis of
a combat aircraft. Its main contribution to a VTOL
fighter was to confirm that multiple engines were
not the answer.*

The SC.1 had five engines, one for forward thrust and four for lift. While this arrangement worked, it had a huge weight penalty that reduced the useful load.

When first flown the SC.1 had only its forward thrust engine fitted. With all lift engines running the vertical thrust was only 4.89kN (1100lb-thrust) greater than the aircraft weight.

Both SC.1s are preserved, XG900 at the Fleet Air Arm Museum at Yeovilton, Somerset, and XG905 at the Ulster Folk and Transport Museum in Northern Ireland.

SIKORSKY VS-300 (1939)

I gor Sikorsky had built two experimental and only partly successful
helicopters in Russia in 1909–10. He emigrated to the USA and his
company built worthy flying boats and landplanes. Returning to rotorcraft
in 1937 he received US Army funding and began work on the VS-300, a
skeletal craft with a three-bladed main rotor and a tail rotor to counteract
torque. On 14 Sept 1939 Igor Sikorsky himself made the first tethered flight.
It was only 10 seconds in duration and there was excessive vibration, but by
November the VS-300 was making much longer flights and the vibration was
reduced to acceptable levels. In May 1941 the VS-300 broke the helicopter
endurance record with a flight of one hour 32 minutes.

The larger VS-316 followed, then the R-4 with a fabric-covered fuselage,
which became the US Army's first service helicopter.

SPECIFICATIONS

CREW:	one
POWERPLANT:	one 75kW (100hp) Franklin four cylinder piston engine
MAX SPEED:	approx 80km/h (50mph)
MAX ALTITUDE:	unknown
SPAN:	9.1m (30ft 0in)
LENGTH:	8.53m (27ft 11in)
HEIGHT:	3.05m (10ft 0in)
WEIGHT:	loaded 522kg (1150lb)

*The VS-300 was a minimalist machine that formed the basis
of the most successful helicopter of World War II, the R-4.
Its configuration was copied by most post-war light and
medium helicopters.*

The VS-300 was unstable and difficult to fly, and had no engine or flight instruments at all. Igor Sikorsky himself flew most of the flight trials and can be recognized in photographs by his Homburg hat.

The VS-300 helped develop the collective and cyclic control systems essential for controlling a helicopter, particularly in the hover.

Later in its flight test programme the VS-300 received a partial fabric covering and began to look more like a conventional helicopter.

When first flown the VS-300 had small rotors on outrigger arms for stability, but these were later replaced with a tail rotor on the left side and it was redesignated the VS-300A.

SUD-EST SE 212 DURANDAL (1956)

A rising from studies for a lightweight mixed-powerplant interceptor, the SE.212 Durandal began life in 1951-52. It was a classic delta with a 60-degree swept wing and an intake in the nose for the Atar turbojet engine. Either a booster rocket and its fuel or an additional jet fuel tank could be fitted under the rear fuselage. It was not until 20 April 1956 that the Durandal flew, as it had been delayed by the company's concentration on the Caravelle airliner. When the firms Sud-Est and Sud-Ouest amalgamated to form Sud Aviation in March 1957 the project was dropped, including completion of the unfinished improved Durandal IV prototype. In May the air force ordered the Mirage IIIA. The second SE.212 had only just flown and it was tested for a little longer, but the programme ended in 1958.

SPECIFICATIONS

CREW:	one
POWERPLANT:	one 37.26kN (8377lb-thrust) SNECMA Atar 10F and one 7.35kN (1653lb-thrust) SEPR 75 rocket motor
MAX SPEED:	1667km/h (1036mph)
MAX ALTITUDE:	unknown
SPAN:	7.4m (24ft 5in)
LENGTH:	12.07m (39ft 7.25in)
HEIGHT:	unknown
WEIGHT:	loaded 6700kg (14,770lb)

Very similar in configuration to the Convair XF-92 of 1948, the Durandal was smaller and somewhat faster, due to its auxiliary rocket motor. It was less practical than the Mirage III, and was a victim of industry rationalization.

If it had entered service, the Durandal would have been armed with two 30mm (1.18in) cannon and a single R 052 air-to-air missile on the centreline.

The SEPR rocket was mounted under the rear fuselage in a detachable pack which also contained the fuel tanks and pumps. This allowed the rocket to be fuelled away from the aircraft, a much safer procedure.

The Durandal achieved Mach 1.57 (1667km/h) with the rocket lit. Without it the aircraft was still able to reach Mach 1.36 (1444km/h).

SUD-EST SE.5000 BAROUDEUR (1953)

One of the many concepts for overcoming runway destruction in wartime was France's Baroudeur, designed to operate from almost any surface. Using a detachable trolley, the Baroudeur, which first flew on 1 August 1953, demonstrated the ability to fly from rough fields, sand and pebble beaches, mud and snow-covered ground. On a good surface it was able to take off on its built-in skid. Three SE.5000s were built, differing mainly in engine power. The French Air Ministry ordered three improved SE.5003 models preparatory to a large production order. This never materialized for political and economic reasons. The proposed improved SE.5004 lost out to the Fiat G.91 in the NATO competition for a standard ground-attack aircraft.

The Super Mystère and Mirage IIIA were soon to appear, and Baroudeur development was dropped in late 1957.

SPECIFICATIONS (SE 5003.1)

CREW:	one
POWERPLANT:	one 36.30kN (8157lb-thrust) SNECMA Atar 101E-4 turbojet engine
MAX SPEED:	1033km/h (642mph)
MAX ALTITUDE:	unknown
SPAN:	10m (32ft 10in)
LENGTH:	13.66m (44ft 10in)
HEIGHT:	(on skids) 3.25m (10ft 8in)
WEIGHT:	maximum 7150kg (15,763lb)

Baroudeur *was a French-Arabic word from the Foreign Legion meaning 'battler' or 'warrior', and the little fighter proved able to operate from any surface put before it. The battle for a production contract was lost, however.*

The second prototype had increased wing anhedral and a more powerful Atar 101C engine.

The Baroudeur would have been armed with two Hispano 603 30mm (1.18in) cannon in the lower nose and could carry various bomb and rocket combinations on wing pylons.

The take-off trolley had a tricycle layout with soft low-pressure tyres and a braking system so the Baroudeur could be taxied like a normal aircraft.

Like the Me 163 Komet, the Baroudeur had a take-off trolley and retractable landing skid. The Baroudeur, however could taxi on its skid back to its trolley.

VFW VAK 191B *(1970)*

The VAK 191B was begun in 1962 as an attempt to replace the Fiat G.91 ground-attack aircraft with a V/TOL nuclear strike bomber. By the time the programme was under way the requirement had changed to one of flexible response rather than all-out retaliation. VAK stood for Vertikalstartendes Auflärungs und Kampfflugzeug (V/STOL Reconnaissance and Strike Aircraft) and the consortium that built it was VFW (Vereinigte Flugtechnische Werke). Preceded by a wingless, skeletal hovering rig using five RB.108 lift engines, the first of three VAK 191Bs was flown free on 10 September 1971 and the first transition to forward flight was made in October 1972; however, soon afterwards the German government withdrew funding. It was refocused as a V/STOL technology demonstrator and flew some useful missions in support of the MRCA (Tornado) programme in 1974–75.

SPECIFICATIONS

CREW:	one
POWERPLANT:	one 45.15kN (10,150lb-thrust) Rolls-Royce/MTU RB193-12 vectored thrust turbofan and two 24.81kN (5587lb-thrust) RB.162-81 turbojet lift engines
MAX SPEED:	1100km/h (684mph)
MAX ALTITUDE:	15,000m (49,213ft)
SPAN:	6.16m (20ft 3in)
LENGTH:	16.40m (53ft 7in)
HEIGHT:	4.30m (14ft 1in)
WEIGHT:	maximum 9000kg (19,845lb)

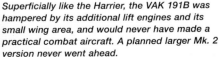

Superficially like the Harrier, the VAK 191B was hampered by its additional lift engines and its small wing area, and would never have made a practical combat aircraft. A planned larger Mk. 2 version never went ahead.

The VAK 191 design team decided against a single vectored thrust engine on the grounds it was too large and heavy for cruising flight, its perceived poor fuel economy and the high drag from the large intakes.

Out of ground effect the VAK-191B benefited from an early form of fly-by-wire control, but suffered from instability in the hover due to re-ingestion of recirculated hot gases.

In addition to the Pegasus-like four-poster vectored thrust main engine, additional lift engines were mounted behind the cockpit and behind the wing. Hinged doors were used for the lift engine intakes and exhausts.

VOUGHT V-173 AND XF5U-1 'FLAPJACK' (1942)

Designer Charles Zimmerman was an advocate of 'discoidal' aircraft from the early 1930s. He joined Chance Vought in 1937 and developed his concepts in stages with little funding. Boone T. Guyton flew the V-173 on 23 November 1942. It was capable of extremely slow flight and short landings and reached quite high speeds for its small engine. Having proved the concept, Vought built the larger XF5U-1 with two (1007kW/1350hp) Pratt & Whitney R-2000-7 radials.

One of the two XF5U-1s was extensively ground tested, but the special propellers were long in coming and propeller-driven fighters were fast going out of fashion. It was planned to flight test the XF5U at Edwards Air Force Base in California, but only a few hops were made at Vought's Connecticut factory before the project was cancelled in March 1947.

SPECIFICATIONS (V-173)

CREW:	one
POWERPLANT:	two 60kW (80hp) Continental A-80 piston engines
MAX SPEED:	222km/h (138mph)
MAX ALTITUDE:	unknown
SPAN:	23ft 4in (7.10m)
LENGTH:	8.12m (26ft 8in)
HEIGHT:	4.51m (14ft 9in)
WEIGHT:	loaded 1.024kg (2.258lb)

The disc-shaped V-173 was the cause of several UFO sightings, and was unofficially dubbed the 'Flapjack'. Production of conventional fighters was given priority and the concept was then overtaken by higher-performing jets.

The skin construction of the XF5U-1 was largely 'Metalite', a Vought-patented composite material made of sandwiched aluminium and balsa wood. The V-173 was a mainly fabric-covered wooden construction.

The V-173 initially used propellers from an F4U-4 Corsair, but to avoid vibration a special set of 'flapping' blades were designed with one pair in each set staggered ahead of the other.

The V-173 is preserved at the Smithsonian, but the two XF5U-1 airframes were broken up when the programme was cancelled.

The proof-of concept V-173 had a fixed undercarriage and small engines driving three-bladed propellers. The outwardly similar XF5U-1s had retracting gear and two powerful radials with four-blade props.

YAKOVLEV YAK-141 'FREESTYLE' (1987)

Known by the manufacturer's designation Yak-141 and the Western reporting name 'Freestyle', this innovative aircraft would have been the Yak-41 if it had reached Russian Navy service. Work began in 1975, but budgetary and technical difficulties, particularly with the engine, delayed a first flight until March 1987, flown by Andrei Sinitsin. The second prototype flew in April 1989 and crashed aboard the carrier *Gorshkov* in October 1991. During testing it set several records for VTOL aircraft, including a time to climb to 12,000m (39,372ft) of 116.15 seconds. Development had virtually stopped by the time the Yak-141 appeared at the 1992 Farnborough Air Show. A land-based STO/VL version was designed, but not developed. The surviving Yak-141 is in the Monino museum in Moscow.

SPECIFICATIONS

CREW:	one
POWERPLANT:	one 152.00kN (34,171lb-thrust) Kobchenko/Soyuz R-79-300 vectored-thrust afterburning turbofan and two 41.78kN (9392lb-thrust) Rybinsk RD- 41 turbofan lift engines
MAX SPEED:	Mach 1.8
MAX ALTITUDE:	over 15,000m (48,215ft)
SPAN:	10.11m (33ft 2in)
LENGTH:	18.36m (60ft 3in)
HEIGHT:	5.00m (16ft 4in)
WEIGHT:	maximum 19,500kg (42,990lb)

The Yak-141 was the most technically successful Russian aircraft and was the first VSTOL aircraft to achieve sustained supersonic flight. The financial difficulties of the 1990s prevented its further development.

The structure of the Yak-141 had more composites than previous Russian combat aircraft, up to 28 per cent by weight being carbon fibre. The remainder of the structure was mainly aluminium lithium alloys.

The Yak-141 was innovative in its lift/cruise nozzle engine system. After the programme was over, Yakovlev and Lockheed Martin collaborated on studies that contributed to the X-35 JSF, which has a similar swivelling nozzle.

The mobile rear nozzle rotated to 90 degrees for vertical flight and to 95 degrees to give braking or reverse flight. The lift engines in the forward fuselage also swivelled for short take-offs or braking.

YAKOVLEV YAK-36 'FREEHAND' (1964)

In 1961 the Yakovlev design bureau was instructed to begin work on a VTOL combat aircraft, using a vectored thrust version of the new R27-300 turbojet, then in development for what would become the MiG-23 fighter. The aircraft that emerged had two of these engines mounted side-by-side in the fuselage, fed by a nose intake and exiting from swivelling nozzles under the wing roots. On 27 July 1964 the first conventional take-off was made by Yuri Garnayev, and on 24 March 1966 the Yak-36 made its first complete transition from a vertical take-off to fast wing-borne flight and a vertical landing. The Yak-36 later made a few trial operations from the helicopter carrier *Moskva* and, although it never entered service, the Yak-36 provided much valuable data for the Yak-38 'Forger', originally called the Yak-36M, even though this bore more resemblance to the Harrier than to the original Yak-36.

SPECIFICATIONS

CREW:	one
POWERPLANT:	two 51.96kN (11,685lb-thrust) Tumanskii R27V-300 lift engines
MAX SPEED:	620mph (1000km/h)
MAX ALTITUDE:	12,000m (39,350ft)
SPAN:	10.5m (34ft 5in)
LENGTH:	including probe 17.0m (55ft 9in)
HEIGHT:	4.5m (14ft 9in)
WEIGHT:	maximum 8900kg (19,625lb)

Three Yak-36s were built (nos 36, 37 and 38), and they received the Nato reporting name 'Freehand', although none was ever seen outside Soviet borders.

The long nose probe was not for flight test instrumentation, but carried the forward set of puffer jets for pitch control. There were also reaction control nozzles in the wingtips.

Like the later Yak-36M 'Forger', the Freehand had a system that automatically fired the ejection seat if the descent rate or other parameters exceeded their safe maximums.

A large door swung down in front of the nose gear to allow more air to reach the engines during hovering flight, when the need was greatest.

WINGS AND THINGS

Swept wings, delta wings, swing wings, forward-swept wings, canards and all-wing designs are just some of the unusual configurations which have been tested on experimental aircraft before entering production.

Good ideas have a habit of coming back. When the forward-swept wing (FSW) Sukhoi Berkut appeared in the 1990s, many said it was a knock-off of the X-29. In fact Russia's own Tsybin LL-3 of 1947 can be considered the first FSW fighter.

The canard foreplane was a feature of the Wright Flyer. It reappeared again in the 1970s and 1980s, firstly on the Saab Viggen and then on testbeds like the F-15 SMTD. Apart from American types, it seems that most current and prototype combat aircraft feature canard foreplanes.

Flying wings and tailless designs date back to the 1930s, and several promising machines were flown during World War II. The full potential of the low-drag and high-lift flying-wing was hampered by control difficulties and official caution, and it was only after the development of advanced computerized fly-by-wire controls that the B-2 Spirit bomber could be built to exploit the low radar signature inherent in flying wing designs.

Left: The F-15 SMTD, designed to be inherently unstable and to be kept in trim by computerized fly-by-wire controls.

AMBROSINI SAGITTARIO (1953)

The Ambrosini Sagittario (Archer), first flown on 5 January 1953, was a transonic aerodynamic research vehicle. With all wooden construction and a 3.92kN (882lb-thrust) Turboméca Marboré turbojet its performance was limited. The all-metal Sagittario 2 was developed using the same aerodynamics and basic layout, replacing the tiny engine with a useful Rolls-Royce Derwent 9. First flown on 19 May 1956, it became the first Italian aircraft to reach Mach 1 on 4 December, flown by Giovanni Franchini. Development of an improved version called the Aerfer Ariete (Battering Ram) reached the prototype stage, but the proposed Leone (Lion) fighter based on this was never built. The Sagittario 2 is displayed at the Italian Air Force Museum at Vigna di Valle just outside Rome.

SPECIFICATIONS (Sagittario II)

CREW:	one
POWERPLANT:	one 16.01kN (3600lb-thrust) Rolls-Royce Derwent 9 turbojet engine
MAX SPEED:	1006km/h (625mph)
MAX ALTITUDE:	14,000m (45,932ft)
SPAN:	7.50m (24ft 7in)
LENGTH:	8.50m (27ft 11in)
HEIGHT:	2.02m (6ft 8in)
WEIGHT:	maximum 3293kg (7260lb)

The post-war Italian aircraft industry caught up again with modern practices with the Sagittario. The Sagittario 2 was the first Italian-designed aircraft to go supersonic.

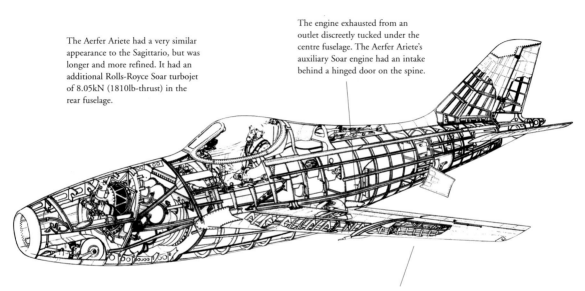

The Aerfer Ariete had a very similar appearance to the Sagittario, but was longer and more refined. It had an additional Rolls-Royce Soar turbojet of 8.05kN (1810lb-thrust) in the rear fuselage.

The engine exhausted from an outlet discreetly tucked under the centre fuselage. The Aerfer Ariete's auxiliary Soar engine had an intake behind a hinged door on the spine.

The Sagittarios and their derivatives had essentially the same wing and horizontal tail surfaces with 45 degrees sweepback.

AMBROSINI SS.3 AND SS.4 (1939)

Ambrosini's chief designer, Sergio Stefanutti, became interested in the concept of aircraft with canard foreplanes and rear mounted wings in the 1930s. The company's previous designs had been elegant and streamlined but conventional monoplanes, largely of wooden construction. Stefanutti's first canard was the SS.3 of 1937, powered by a tiny 28kW (38hp) CNA IIbis two-cylinder engine. The SS.3 flew well, but was hampered by its lack of power. The larger follow-on SS.4 made a successful flight on 7 March 1939, but an engine failure the following day caused it to crash on its second flight, killing test pilot Ambrogio Colombo. The crash was an excuse for the authorities to cancel the canard fighter project and direct Ambrosini and Stefanutti to concentrate on the company's more conventional fighter designs.

SPECIFICATIONS (SS.4)

CREW:	one
POWERPLANT:	one 716kW (960hp) Isotta-Fraschini Asso XI R.C.40 piston engine
MAX SPEED:	estimated 540km/h (336mph)
MAX ALTITUDE:	unknown
SPAN:	12.32m (40ft 5in)
LENGTH:	6.74m (22ft 1in)
HEIGHT:	2.48m (8ft 1in)
WEIGHT:	maximum 2446kg (5401lb)

The first and least-known of the canard fighters of the war years, the SS.4 had considerable potential, but was a victim of an accident unrelated to its radical design.

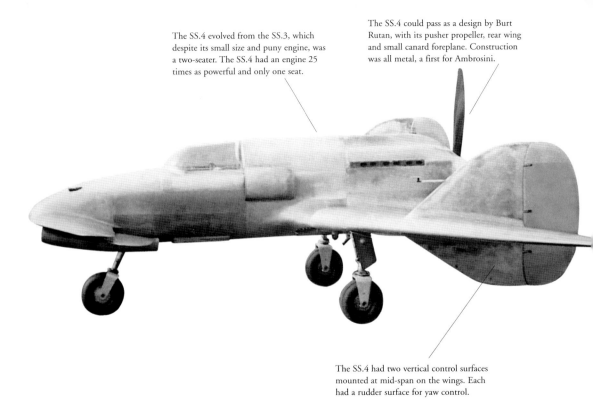

The SS.4 evolved from the SS.3, which despite its small size and puny engine, was a two-seater. The SS.4 had an engine 25 times as powerful and only one seat.

The SS.4 could pass as a design by Burt Rutan, with its pusher propeller, rear wing and small canard foreplane. Construction was all metal, a first for Ambrosini.

The SS.4 had two vertical control surfaces mounted at mid-span on the wings. Each had a rudder surface for yaw control.

ARMSTRONG WHITWORTH A.W.52 (1947)

With an eventual goal of a flying-wing airliner in mind, designer John Lloyd began work in 1942 on the laminar-flow A.W.52 for Armstrong Whitworth. The first AW.52, serial TS363, first flew on 13 November 1947, having been preceded by a half-scale tandem-seat glider, the A.W.52G. TS363 went out of control and crashed due to flutter in May 1949. Pilot J.O. Lancaster became the first airman in the UK to escape using a Martin-Baker ejection seat. The Derwent-powered second aircraft (TS368) flew in 1948 and was mainly used in laminar-flow research with a boundary layer suction flow system to 'blow' the control surfaces for increased effectiveness at low speeds. Another system provided anti-icing warm air over the forward part of the wing. This innovative aircraft was not preserved when the Royal Aeronautical Establishment finished with it in 1954.

SPECIFICATIONS (first aircraft)

CREW:	one
POWERPLANT:	two 22.4kN (5000lb thrust) Rolls-Royce Nene I turbojet engines
MAX SPEED:	805km/h (500mph)
MAX ALTITUDE:	unknown
SPAN:	27.43m (90ft)
LENGTH:	11.38m (37ft 4in)
HEIGHT:	unknown
WEIGHT:	maximum 15,490kg (34,150lb)

Nothing quite as radical as the AW.52 ever entered RAF or airline service. Testing uncovered the difficulties of maintaining large laminar-flow surfaces.

The wingtips carried the rudders, which operated differentially. When one was turned inwards 10 degrees, the other rudder turned outwards by 30 degrees.

A large single flap was mounted on the centre-section trailing edge and had cut-outs for the engine exhausts when in the down position.

The elevons worked symmetrically as elevators and differentially as ailerons.

The wings had a very smooth laminar-flow surface with less than 0.05mm variation. They were very susceptible to imperfections, which caused loss of efficiency.

RG324

BELL X-5 *(1951)*

Based very closely on a captured Messerschmitt prototype called the P.1101, the X-5 was the first aircraft to explore the possibilities of variable-geometry wings. Two X-5s were built. The first flew in the hands of Jean Ziegler on 20 June 1951. The second failed to pull out of a spin in October 1953 and crashed, killing the pilot. The small engine made for poor stall characteristics at high sweep. Plans to develop the X-5 into a fighter were rejected mainly because of its small size, although studies were made into installing gun armament. Variable geometry was tested on the unsuccessful XF10F Jaguar of 1952, but otherwise largely abandoned until the 1960s. The first X-5 made 153 flights in the hands of 12 pilots, mainly Joe Walker and 'Skip' Ziegler, and is displayed today at the USAF Museum in Ohio.

SPECIFICATIONS

CREW:	one
POWERPLANT:	one 21.80kN (4900lb-thrust) Allison J35-A-17A turbojet engine
MAX SPEED:	1135 km/h (705mph)
MAX ALTITUDE:	12,802m (42,000ft)
SPAN:	spread 10.21m (33ft 6in)
LENGTH:	10.18m (33ft 4.5in)
HEIGHT:	3.66m (12ft 0in)
WEIGHT:	gross 4479kg (9875lb)

After its experimental career was over the X-5 proved useful as a chase aircraft for other programmes, due to its wide speed range.

The wing swept from 20 to 60 degrees using electric motors. A manual back-up system could be engaged in the case of electrical failure.

The engine was slung under the main structure, giving the possibility of a variety of engine choices, but in the end the low-powered J35 was the only one to be used.

Air brakes were mounted either side of the nose behind the intake. These were deemed necessary to aid control at the X-5's maximum wing sweep.

BOEING BIRD OF PREY *(1996)*

The Bird of Prey was a secret project to demonstrate new stealth and manufacturing technologies using a subsonic test platform.

The programme was begun in 1992 by a team at McDonnell Douglas. By the time it was revealed publicly in October 2002 and donated to the USAF Museum in Ohio, Boeing had taken over McDonnell Douglas and the aircraft had become known as the Boeing Bird of Prey. No other US military or manufacturer's designation is known. The single demonstrator made only 38 test flights between the autumn of 1996 and 1999, when the programme ended. The Bird of Prey embodied a range of stealth concepts that were a generation beyond those of the F-117. It also pioneered new 'lean manufacturing' methods. Some aspects of its configuration have found their way into proposed future unmanned combat air vehicles (UCAVs) such as the Boeing X-45.

SPECIFICATIONS

CREW:	one
POWERPLANT:	one 14.19kN (3190lb-thrust) Pratt & Whitney JT15D-5C turbofan
MAX SPEED:	about 483km/h (300mph)
MAX ALTITUDE:	6096m (20,000ft)
SPAN:	7.01m (23ft)
LENGTH:	14.33m (47ft)
HEIGHT:	2.82m (9ft 3in)
WEIGHT:	3357kg (7400lb)

The Bird of Prey was successful in being kept secret, although detailed results of its flight tests remain classified. It contributed to the design of unmanned aircraft and to the manufacturing of the F/A-18E/F Super Hornet.

The intake was recessed behind the cockpit and was shaped to produce the lowest radar signature possible. The exhaust was designed to reduce heat signature.

The Bird of Prey was one of the first aerospace programmes to use large, single-piece composite parts, disposable tooling and designed using three-dimensional virtual reality and assembly processes.

The Bird of Prey had no vertical tail, but a small ventral fin and the downturned wingtips provided lateral stability.

BOULTON-PAUL P.111A *(1950)*

Stemming from a 1946 requirement for an aircraft to research high-speed delta wing handling, the P.111 was a compact tailless delta turbojet aircraft of the same general configuration as the XP-92. On 10 October 1950 the one and only P.111 (VT935) was flown at Boscombe Down, Wiltshire. The original fully powered controls and the artificial feel system proved over-sensitive. The P.111 also had three landing accidents. In late 1952 it was modified to the P.111a. The P.120 was a closely related design, albeit with a high-mounted tailplane. Only three weeks after its 1952 first flight it crashed when this failed. The P.111 was retired in June 1958. It has been exhibited at the Midland Air Museum at Coventry since 1975.

SPECIFICATIONS
(with extended wings)

CREW:	one
POWERPLANT:	one 22.69kW (5100lb-thrust) Rolls-Royce Nene 3 turbojet engine
MAX SPEED:	1019km/h (633mph)
MAX ALTITUDE:	unknown
SPAN:	10.21m (33ft 6in)
LENGTH:	9.60in (31ft 6in)
HEIGHT:	3.84m (12ft 7in)
WEIGHT:	original configuration loaded 4354kg (9,599lb)

Despite its intended high-speed research role, the P.111 was not blessed with a very high performance, reducing its utility in researching the full envelope for the delta wing.

The original control system was too sensitive, resulting in pilot-induced oscillations. The later change to a fully geared system allowed precise control at high speeds.

During tests, the wingtip extensions were fitted to evaluate their effect on handling. The original span of 7.82m (25ft 8in) was extended to 9.07m (29ft 9in), then 10.21m (33ft 6in).

As the P.111a, the aircraft had a revised control system, a probe in the intake centrebody, undercarriage changes and the addition of a four-part airbrake on the fuselage.

VT935

CONVAIR XF-92A *(1948)*

Based on the theories of German scientist Dr Alexander Lippisch, the XF-92A evolved from a more radical ramjet-powered XP-92 design which would have housed the pilot in the intake cone. The XF-92A (with a conventional cockpit above the intake) made its official debut flight on 1 April 1948, flown by Sam Shannon, becoming the first pure delta-winged aircraft to fly. Chuck Yeager made many flights in the XF-92A before it was passed to NACA. Scott Crossfield also flew it, but described it as a 'miserable flying beast'. It suffered a nosegear collapse while Crossfield was flying it in October 1953 and was never flown again, being retired to the USAF Museum in Ohio. The XF-92A design was developed into the YF-102, which had its share of problems, but in turn led to the successful F-102 Delta Dagger.

SPECIFICATIONS

CREW:	one
POWERPLANT:	one 33.36kN (7500lb-thrust) Allison J33-A-23 afterburning turbojet engine
MAX SPEED:	1127km/h (700mph)
MAX ALTITUDE:	15,476m (50,750ft)
SPAN:	12.89m (31ft 4in)
LENGTH:	12.95m (42ft 6in)
HEIGHT:	5.43m (17ft 9in)
WEIGHT:	maximum 6626kg (14,608lb)

Testing of the XF-92A, the design of which was based heavily on wartime German research, contributed to the understanding of delta wings, which found a wide application in subsequent combat aircraft.

The XF-92A first flew with a 20.46kN (4600lb-thrust) Allison engine, later upgraded to 23.13kN (5200lb-thrust) and 37.81kN (8500lb-thrust) versions. It was subsonic in level flight.

One unusual use for the XF-92A was portraying a fictional 'MiG-23' fighter in the Howard Hughes' film *Test Pilot*. Unfortunately, when the film finally appeared in 1957, scenes showing the XF-92A ended up on the cutting-room floor.

One problem discovered with the delta wing configuration was a tendency to pitch up without pilot command. Experience with the XF-92A led to corrective measures which helped Convair's later delta wing aircraft, including the Sea Dart, Delta Dagger and Hustler.

243

DASSAULT MIRAGE G *(1967)*

Built as part of an Anglo-French requirement for a variable-geometry strike aircraft, the Mirage G was Europe's first foray into 'swing wings'. Apart from the wings, the design was largely that of the Mirage F2, an unsuccessful larger two-seat version of the F1. The original Mirage G was flown on 18 November 1967 with a single Pratt & Whitney turbofan. It reached Mach 2.1 and had more than 400 flight hours before it crashed in January 1971. The first twin-engined Mirage G8 (the two-seat G8.01) was flown in May 1971, followed by the single-seat G8.02 in July 1972.

The Armée de l'Air concluded that variable geometry was not worth the weight penalty, although other air arms disagreed. The G8.01 is in the Musée de l'Air collection near Paris.

SPECIFICATIONS

CREW:	two
POWERPLANT:	two 70.61kN (15,873lb-thrust) SNECMA Atar 9K-50 turbojet engines
MAX SPEED:	2495km/h (1550mph)
MAX ALTITUDE:	unknown
SPAN:	spread 13.00m (42ft 7.75in)
LENGTH:	16.80m (55ft 1.5in)
HEIGHT:	5.35m (17ft 6.5in)
WEIGHT:	max 23,800kg (52,470lb)

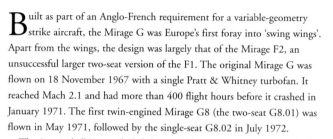

Built in three versions with single or twin engines and one or two seats, the Mirage Gs seemed to prove that variable geometry was impractical. Several Soviet, American and European manufacturers chose to differ.

Dassault also evaluated a Mirage F8 version with fixed-geometry wings at 55 degrees sweep, but returned to delta wings for its next production fighter, the Mirage 2000.

The Mirage G.8 was proposed as a multi-role fighter with a Cyrano IV multi-mode radar and a low-altitude navigation and attack system. It would have been capable of long-range interception as well as reconnaissance and attack missions.

The wing swept between 23 degrees for take-off and landing, and low-speed flight, and a maximum of 70 degrees for high-speed operation.

DASSAULT MIRAGE I *(1955)*

A 1954 specification called for a small supersonic interceptor capable of reaching 18,000m (60,000ft) in six minutes. Dassault's MD.550 Mystère Delta flew on 25 June 1955. It had nothing in common with the swept-wing Mystère series. During 1956 it was rebuilt with shorter-span wings, a shorter fuselage and a new windscreen, and became the Mirage I. A centreline pylon could carry a single AAM. A SEPR 66 rocket motor was added, and the Mirage I's top speed was boosted to Mach 1.6 with the rocket motor compared to Mach 1.3 without it.

It was realized the Mirage I was too small for much further development, and the radar-equipped second prototype (named the Mirage II) was cancelled before completion. The enlarged single-engined Mirage III was developed into one of the most successful warplane families of all time.

SPECIFICATIONS

CREW:	one
POWERPLANT:	two 9.61kN (2160lb-thrust) Dassault MD.30R (Rolls-Royce Viper) turbojets and (later) one 14.71kN (3307lb-thrust) SEPR 66 rocket motor
MAX SPEED:	1700km/h (1056mph)
MAX ALTITUDE:	unknown
SPAN:	7.30m (23ft 11in)
LENGTH:	11.10m (36ft 5in)
HEIGHT:	unknown
WEIGHT:	loaded 5070kg (11,177lb)

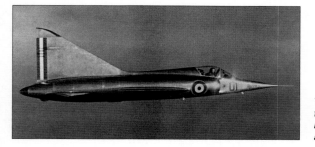

The Mirage I set the template for French fighter development for the next 50 years, the majority of Dassault's subsequent combat aircraft being variations on a delta wing.

The performance requirements of the Armée de l'Air allowed the MD.550/Mirage I the capacity to have a radar or a missile, but not both. As such it was not a practical warplane, but taught the French a great deal about delta wing design and handling.

When rebuilt to Mirage I standard, the MD.550's engines were given primitive afterburners with 'eyelid' type nozzles and a SEPR 66 booster rocket motor was fitted in a ventral fin.

As initially flown the MD.550 had a very broad chord fin. This was reduced in size and given a swept back trailing edge in the Mirage I.

DE HAVILLAND DH.110 *(1951)*

The De Havilland DH.110 was developed for both Royal Air Force and Fleet Air Arm service, although the FAA had changed its requirement by the time the first prototype WG236 flew on 26 September 1951, piloted by John Cunningham. The DH.110 was the first twin-engined two-seat aircraft to go supersonic (in a dive).

The prototype WG236 broke up in flight during a supersonic dive over the Farnborough airshow in Hampshire, in September 1952, killing John Derry, Tony Richards and 28 spectators.

The second DH.110 (WG240) was grounded until it could be strengthened and modified with an all-moving tailplane, a smaller ventral fin and cambered wing leading-edge extensions. With the addition of an arrestor hook, this aircraft was used for carrier trials, the success of which saw the FAA adopt a navalized version as the Sea Vixen.

SPECIFICATIONS

CREW:	two
POWERPLANT:	two 33.43kN (7500lb-thrust) Rolls-Royce Avon turbojet engines
MAX SPEED:	Mach 1.0 in a dive
MAX ALTITUDE:	unknown
SPAN:	15.25m (50ft 0in)
LENGTH:	15.88m (52ft 2in)
HEIGHT:	3.28m (10ft 9in)
WEIGHT:	unknown

The break-up of the first DH.110 led to a greater understanding of airframe stresses at transonic speeds. The RAF chose the Javelin fighter after the accident, but eventually the Royal Navy got the superior Sea Vixen, based on the DH.110.

The Farnborough crash was attributed to separation of the outer wing panels under high loads. These areas were greatly strengthened before the second aircraft resumed the test programme.

The pilot's canopy was offset to the port side to allow the radar operator to sit below and beside him in a compartment with only a small window and skylight.

Navalizing the second DH.110 prototype saw powered folding wings fitted, an arrestor hook installed and the introduction of a heavier undercarriage with hydraulic nosewheel steering.

DORNIER DO 24TT (1983)

The company founded by Claudius Dornier was noted for its flying boats, including the enormous Do X of 1929. One of the Luftwaffe's best patrol and rescue aircraft was the Do 24, first built in 1937. After World War II, Dornier moved its aircraft development work to Spain, where some Do 24s had been licence-built. A Do 24T-3 built in Spain in 1943 and which served with the Spanish Air Force until 1970 was sold back to Dornier in 1971. Between 1979 and 1983, it was converted to Do 24TT configuration as a project to revive the flying boat using modern technologies. Flying again in 1983, the DO 24TT was successfully tested, but failed to find a market. Retired to a museum, it was resurrected again by Iren Dornier, Claudius's grandson, and began a world goodwill tour in 2004.

SPECIFICATIONS

CREW:	two
POWERPLANT:	three 875kW (1173hp) Pratt & Whitney Canada PT6A-45B turboprop engines
MAX SPEED:	438km/h (272mph)
MAX ALTITUDE:	unknown
SPAN:	30.0m (98ft 3in)
LENGTH:	21.95m (72ft 0in)
HEIGHT:	5.65m (18ft 6in)
WEIGHT:	maximum 14,000kg (30,865lb)

The Do 24TT was a modernized amphibian version of an efficient flying-boat design of the 1930s. It failed to revive the market, but demonstrated greatly improved efficiency and continues to act as a technology demonstrator.

The two Bramo Fafnir piston engines were replaced by three PT6 turboprops, and a high-tech supercritical wing replaced the original.

The wing was increased in span by 3m (9ft 10in) during the conversion. The basic design with its curved tips is also used on the Fairchild Dornier 328 and 328JET.

The Do 24TT has a conventional undercarriage housed in the nose and in the side sponsons, thus allowing operations from land. The original Do 24 was a pure flying boat.

F+W N 20 AIGUILLON (1951)

To replace its wartime propeller-driven fighters still in service, Switzerland's Federal Aviation Factory (F+W) at Emmen embarked on an ambitious project to develop a tailless jet fighter designated the N-20 and named Aiguillon (Sting). Clearly influenced by the Vought F7U-1 Cutlass of 1948, the Aiguillon had one fin rather than two, and had four engines with intakes in the wing leading edges. To test the concept, a three-fifths scale demonstrator called the Arbalete (Crossbow) was flown in 1951 with four tiny 1.08kN (242lb-thrust) Turboméca turbojets. The Aiguillon itself was less successful. Taxiing trials began in 1952, and in the course of these the N-20 made several short hops. In March, however, the Aiguillon was grounded without having really flown. The government was alarmed at the large cost of the project, which would not be recouped by export sales due to Swiss neutrality. The N-20 is preserved in the Dubendorf museum near Zurich.

SPECIFICATIONS

CREW:	one
POWERPLANT:	four 9.4kN (2113lb-thrust) Armstrong-Siddeley Swiss-Mamba SM-01 turbofan engines
MAX SPEED:	estimated 720km/h (447mph)
MAX ALTITUDE:	estimated 8000m (26,247ft)
SPAN:	12.50m (41ft 0in)
LENGTH:	12.50m (41ft 0in)
HEIGHT:	3.67m (12ft 0in)
WEIGHT:	loaded 9000kg (19,845lb)

The radical Aiguillon was a remarkable design for an industry that had been bypassed by wartime developments. Its four engines and tailless layout were innovative for a fighter, but the Swiss chose instead to develop the simpler P-16.

The Aiguillon had dual mainwheels as well as nosewheels. It was expected to be able to operate from short or unpaved strips.

The intakes were buried in the wings in the fashion of the Comet airliner and were of an unusual 'eye' shape. The four small engines were deemed insufficient for a reasonable performance, but the project was cancelled before further options could be explored.

The N-20's low-bypass turbofan engines were derived from the Armstrong-Siddeley Mamba turboprop. They were some of the first turbofans used in any aircraft.

253

FAIREY DELTA 1 *(1951)*

The Fairey Delta began as a concept for a ramp-launched rocket fighter along the lines of the German Bachem Natter. To test the aerodynamics, a conventional aerodynamic testbed was ordered. Group Captain R. Gordon Slade made the first Delta flight on 10 March 1951. This followed a long series of taxi trials and the addition of a fixed horizontal surface at the top of the tail to stop serious pitching as it gathered speed.

After being damaged in a landing accident in September 1951, the Delta did not fly again until May 1953. Doubts about its stability remained and it was regarded as dangerous. It was eventually taken to the weapons range at Shoeburyness, Kent, and expended in tests to measure the effects of weapons on modern aircraft structures.

SPECIFICATIONS (VX350)

CREW:	one
POWERPLANT:	one 187kN (42,000lb-thrust) Pratt & Whitney F119-PW-611C afterburning turbofan engine
MAX SPEED:	Mach 1.8
MAX ALTITUDE:	13,716m (45,000ft)
SPAN:	13.12m (43ft)
LENGTH:	50ft 11in (15.52m)
HEIGHT:	4.60m (15ft 2in)
WEIGHT:	loaded 17,485kg (38,549lb)

Only one of the two planned Fairey Deltas (retrospectively designated the Fairey Delta 1) was built, and it achieved relatively little other than being the first British delta-winged aircraft.

When it returned to flight after its 1951 accident, the FD.1 had lost its leading-edge slats and the housings for its wingtip anti-spin parachutes.

The large control surfaces made the FD.1 hard to fly with precision, but gave it a very rapid roll rate. The additional tail surface restricted the top speed to under 555km/h (345mph), making it useless for high-speed research.

Even when flown as a jet testbed it was planned to fit four rocket boosters with a combined 22.24kN (5500lb-thrust). These were never actually fitted.

GENERAL DYNAMICS F-16 AFTI *(1982)*

In order to evaluate unconventional control methods, the Advanced Fighter Technology Integration (AFTI) F-16 was commissioned in 1978. The platform was 75-0750, the sixth Full-Scale Development (FSD) F-16. The first flight in AFTI configuration was on 10 July 1982 , made by General Dynamics pilot Alex Wolfe. A bulged spine housed extra avionics, which included a triple-redundant Digital Flight Control System (DFCS), which together with the canard foreplanes permitted flat turns without banking.

The AFTI was used to test a variety of technologies, including voice activation of some of the avionics suite, a helmet-mounted sighting system and a Forward Looking Infra Red (FLIR). This long-serving F-16 was later used for various other programmes, the last of which was to test electric actuators for the JSF programme. When these tests were done it was retired to the USAF Museum collection in Ohio.

Although vertical canard foreplanes did not catch on, technologies tested in the F-16 AFTI, such as voice-activated systems and helmet-mounted sights, have become common on the latest generation of fighters.

SPECIFICATIONS

CREW:	one
POWERPLANT:	one 64.90kN (14,590lb-thrust) Pratt & Whitney-PW-200 afterburning turbofan engine
MAX SPEED:	2145km/h (1333mph)
MAX ALTITUDE:	unknown
SPAN:	9.45m (31ft 0in)
LENGTH:	14.52m (47ft 8in)
HEIGHT:	5.01m (16ft 5in)
WEIGHT:	loaded 11,094kg (24,459lb)

A helmet-mounted target designation sight could be used to designate targets. The FLIR seeker and radar could be automatically slaved to follow the pilot's head movement.

The F-16 AFTI had a Voice-Controlled Interactive Device (VCID), which controlled many of the avionics. Up to 90 per cent of spoken commands from a dictionary of up to 256 words could be recognized, even under high *g* forces.

The canard foreplanes under the intake had come from a previous programme, the F-16 CCV (Control Configured Vehicle), which had used one of the very first F-16 prototypes.

GENERAL DYNAMICS F-111 MAW *(1985)*

The variable-geometry F-111 'Aardvark' bomber proved suitable for a variety of experiments with its easily replaceable wing, and NASA operated several pre-production F-111As on test work. The most modified of these (63-9778) joined NASA as the Transonic Aircraft Technology Test Aircraft in 1972. It was fitted with a short-span broader supercritical wing and flown from 1974 to 1980 in this configuration. It was then given laminar-flow wing gloves. The biggest change was a Boeing-built 'Mission Adaptive Wing' (MAW). The theory behind this was that a flexible camber wing could be reconfigured before and during flight to optimize flight characteristics at different speeds and altitudes. In MAW configuration 63-9778 first flew in October 1985, conducting a test programme until early 1989. It has since been stored at Edwards Air Force Base, California, as part of the Air Force Flight Test Centre (AFFTC) collection.

SPECIFICATIONS

CREW:	two
POWERPLANT:	two 82.3kN (18,500lb-thrust) Pratt & Whitney TF30-P-3 afterburning turbofans
MAX SPEED:	over 2124km/h (1320mph) or Mach 2.0
MAX ALTITUDE:	unknown
SPAN:	spread 19.20m (63ft 0in)
LENGTH:	23.02m (75ft 6.5in)
HEIGHT:	5.20m (17ft 0.5in)
WEIGHT:	maximum 34,473kg (76,000lb)

Also known as the F-111 AFTI (Advanced Fighter Technology Integration) after the name of a joint NASA/USAF programme, NASA's Aardvark collected promising data on fully variable camber wings.

The F-111 MAW's leading and trailing edges were made of internally articulated flexible fibreglass sections, which gave the smoothest surface along the span as they lowered and retracted.

Dark bands on the wing were areas of pressure orifices that measured local surface pressures and locations of the shock wave at different speeds.

No manned aircraft have yet been built with a Mission Adaptive Wing, but the F-111's MAW research is being used to design future 'morphing' unmanned aerial vehicles (UAVs).

GOTHA GO 229/HORTEN HO IX (1945)

Walter and Reimar Horten built a series of tailless flying wing gliders and piston-engine aircraft from 1936–40. In 1943 they received official permission to build a prototype for a jet-powered fighter version designated the Ho IX. The first prototype (V1) was a glider and flew in February 1944. The flying characteristics were good and with the long-delayed jets fitted maximum altitude was expected to be over 15,200m (50,000ft), an unheard of figure in 1945. The Jumo 004-powered Horten IX V2 made its first flight at Oranienburg on 2 February 1945. Test pilot Erwin Ziller was killed two weeks later following an engine failure and loss of control. Development of a production version was entrusted to Gothaer Waggonfabrik (Gotha), and it was working on several further prototypes and pre-production models of the slightly larger Go 229 fighter when the war ended.

SPECIFICATIONS (Go 229A-0)

CREW:	
POWERPLANT:	two 8.73m (1962lb-thrust) Junkers 004B-1 turbojet engines
MAX SPEED:	estimated 977km/h (607mph)
MAX ALTITUDE:	16,000m (52,500ft)
SPAN:	16.80m (55ft 1in)
LENGTH:	7.50m (24ft 7in)
HEIGHT:	2.80m (9ft 2in)
WEIGHT:	loaded 7507kg (16,550lb)

Only three flights were made by the futuristic Ho IX before World War II ended. One unfinished example was captured with its wings detached and is awaiting restoration for display at the National Air and Space Museum in Washington D.C.

The Go 229 V3 was captured complete but unflown at the factory. It was taken back to the USA for analysis, and today is in storage for eventual restoration and display by the National Air and Space Museum.

The huge front wheel came from a Heinkel He 177 and the main undercarriage was originally that of a Messerschmitt Me 109G.

Despite its futuristic looks, the Go 229 was constructed with 1930s methods of welded steel-tube structure skinned with plywood. The outer sections were all wood, with leading edges of resin-impregnated moulded sections.

GRUMMAN X-29 *(1984)*

The Defense Advanced Projects Agency (DARPA) awarded Grumman a contract in 1981 to develop two demonstrators of a fighter-type aircraft featuring a forward-swept wing (FSW) design. The invention of new composite materials allowed such a wing to be built and flown at supersonic speeds without danger of being ripped off due to aeroelastic twisting. The first X-29 was flown on 14 December 1984 by Charles 'Chuck' Sewell. During its test career the X-29 demonstrated controlled flight at up to 67 degrees angle-of-attack and speeds of up to Mach 1.8. By the time the programme concluded in September 1991, the first aircraft had made 254 flights and the second 120, before the former was retired to display at Edwards Air Force Base, California, and the latter to the USAF Museum.

SPECIFICATIONS

CREW:	one
POWERPLANT:	one 71.17kN (16,000lb-thrust) General Electric F404-GE-400 afterburning turbofan engine
MAX SPEED:	1931km/h (1200mph)
MAX ALTITUDE:	15,300m (50,200ft)
SPAN:	8.20m (27ft 3in)
LENGTH:	with probe 16.40m (53ft 1in)
HEIGHT:	4.30m (14ft 4in)
WEIGHT:	maximum 8072kg (17,303lb)

The successful X-29 programme proved the strength of composite materials and the effectiveness of fly-by-wire control systems. The USA did not build any further FSW aircraft, but the configuration reappeared on the Sukhoi S-37 (Su-47) fighter prototype in 1997.

Composite structures can be built of sheets layered so they will bend in one direction and not another. Their stiffness can be tailored to give the greatest strength in the direction of highest load.

To save money, the X-29s contained many parts taken from other aircraft, including an entire F-5A nose, cockpit and nosegear. The main landing gear and some other parts were from the F-16, and the engine was that used in the F/A-18.

The airflow over a forward-swept wing moves from the tips toward the fuselage, the reverse of a sweptback wing. The FSW wingtips (and ailerons) will stall later than the roots, allowing greater manoeuvrability.

HANDLEY PAGE HP.75 MANX (1943)

H aving studied various configurations for a long-range bomber, including the Westland Pterodactyl type and a canard layout, Handley Page selected a wingless design by Dr Gustav Lachmann in 1942 for further research in the form of a flying testbed or so-called 'rider plane'.

J.F. Marsh made the first flight of the HP.75, later named Manx after the tailless cat, on 25 June 1943, although an inadvertent hop leading to under-carriage damage had happened in September 1942. Keeping the HP.75 in trim proved very difficult, and other stability problems were found. A proposed airliner derivative would have had a canard foreplane, but was never built, although a larger HP.75A 'rider plane' was constructed. The Manx flew only occasionally, making 29 flights by November 1945. The loss of the normal test crew in the crash of the prototype Hermes I in December effectively killed the programme and it flew only twice more. It lingered on in an airworthy condition until December 1946, but was finally scrapped in 1952.

SPECIFICATIONS

CREW:	two
POWERPLANT:	two 104kW (140hp) De Havilland Gipsy Major II piston engines
MAX SPEED:	235km/h (146mph)
MAX ALTITUDE:	3200m (10,500ft)
SPAN:	12.16m (39ft 10in)
LENGTH:	5.56m (18ft 3in)
HEIGHT:	unknown
WEIGHT:	maximum 1814kg (4000lb)

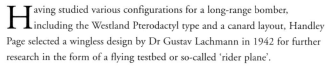

The Manx was intended as a step towards a laminar-flow flying-wing bomber or airliner. Wartime priorities and teething troubles prevented a full test programme, and it remained a sideline to conventional aircraft development at Handley Page.

The Manx had a crew of two: a pilot and a flight test observer, who sat facing the rear. Access to the observer's compartment was through a hinged tailcone.

The Manx layout offered the advantages for a bomber of having pusher engines buried in the wing for low drag and a clear field of fire for heavy armament to be mounted in the rear of the fuselage.

All the undercarriage was originally fixed down, but in 1944 a retracting main gear was added, although the nosegear remained a fixed unit with a faired cover.

HANDLEY PAGE H.P.20 (1921)

Frederick Handley Page was a pioneer in the use of wing slots and slats to delay stalling. In 1920 the Air Ministry directed 'H-P' to modify an Airco D.H.9A biplane with a monoplane wing that featured full-span leading-edge slats and ailerons with slots that opened at their hinges when deflected. The modified aircraft (F1632) first flew on 24 February 1921, designated the X.4B, although there is evidence that the wing might have flown on D.H.9A E8614, which may have been the X.4A. Whichever is the case, an HP.20 was the first monoplane to feature slats, a device in various forms which has continued in use to the present day. The tests were not without hazard and several crashes ensued. The H.P.20 was one of the few biplanes ever converted to a monoplane. Its pioneering work made low-speed flight, particularly landing and take-off, much safer for future generations.

SPECIFICATIONS (DH.9A)

CREW:	one
POWERPLANT:	one 298kW (400hp) Liberty 12A piston engine
MAX SPEED:	approx 183km/h (114mph)
MAX ALTITUDE:	5029m (16,500ft)
SPAN:	14.02m (46ft 0in)
LENGTH:	9.14m (30ft 0in)
HEIGHT:	3.28m (10ft 9in)
WEIGHT:	empty 1270kg (2800lb)

The H.P.20 has not survived, but the subsequent HP.39 Gugnunc (left), designed from the outset to demonstrate slats, is part of the Science Museum collection in London.

Slats and slots increase the effective camber of the wing, making it more efficient at low speeds and high angles of attack. Slats are usually kept in retracted position by the airflow and extend under gravity at slow speed.

The fuel tank was mounted above the wing. The long struts presumably kept the tank clear of the airflow to avoid interference.

When first tested, the HP.20 had a fixed leading edge 'pilot plane', but this was articulated to become a moveable slat, which extended under gravity as the airspeed decreased.

HAWKER P.1081 (1950)

The P.1040 of 1947 was Hawker's first jet aircraft. With refinements it was adopted for service as the Sea Hawk. It was modified as the P.1072 in 1950 with a rocket motor and became Britain's first mixed-powerplant fighter. The P.1052 of 1948 was a separate development of the P.1040, built with a swept wing. It later received a swept tailplane as well. The second of two P.1052s, VX279, was rebuilt as the P.1081, with a swept fin and a single tailpipe rather than the bifurcated unit of its forebears. The impetus for the P.1081 was Australian interest in a new fighter to replace the Meteor. The P.1081 first flew on 19 June 1950.

Australian enthusiasm waned, however, as it was obvious something more radical was needed to better the MiG-15 soon being encountered in Korea. The P.1081 was considered as a basis for the RAF's next fighter, but a larger Avon-powered design known as the P.1067 was clearly superior and flew as the Hunter in July 1951.

SPECIFICATIONS

CREW:	one
POWERPLANT:	one 22.2kN (5000lb-thrust) Rolls-Royce Nene 102 turbojet engine
MAX SPEED:	1118km/h (695mph)
MAX ALTITUDE:	13,899m (45,600ft)
SPAN:	9.60m (31ft 6in)
LENGTH:	11.38m (37ft 4in)
HEIGHT:	4.04m (13ft 3in)
WEIGHT:	loaded 6568kg (14,480lb)

The design of the P.1081 marked the final stage before the Hunter. Although smaller, with a lower-powered engine, it had most of the features that would make the Hunter the most successful British jet export.

The conversion of P.1052 to P.1081 involved removing everything aft of the rear engine bay bulkhead and replacing it with a new unit. The nose section and complete wing was retained.

The bifurcated jet exhausts were replaced by a single 'straight through' jetpipe, requiring a somewhat fatter rear fuselage. A planned afterburner was not fitted and the P.1081 used a jetpipe from a Supermarine Attacker.

The P.1081 had a short life. While flying from Farnborough it crashed on 3 April 1951 near Lewes, East Sussex, and killed chief test pilot T.S. Wade. A definitive cause for the accident was never established.

JUNKERS JU 287 (1944)

German engineer Hans Wocke was the first to propose a forward-swept wing (FSW) for a high-speed jet bomber, as such a layout also gave good handling at low speeds. On 16 August 1944 the Ju 287 V1 (first prototype) flew as a pure aerodynamic testbed for the FSW concept. It had a fixed landing gear and utilized components from several aircraft. The V1 made 17 flights, proving the viability of the concept. As predicted, the wings experienced aeroelastic twisting at high speeds. The V1 reached 650km/h (404mph) in a dive. Higher speeds would have eventually exceeded the structural limits. Before the V2 and V3 prototypes were ready, Soviet troops overran the factory. The V2 was captured intact and taken to the USSR along with its design team, including Wocke, and flew there in 1947.

SPECIFICATIONS

CREW:	three
POWERPLANT:	four 8.83kN (1984lb-thrust) Junkers Jumo 004B turbojet engines and four 11.77kN (2645lb-thrust) Walter 501 booster rockets
MAX SPEED:	558km/h (347mph)
MAX ALTITUDE:	10,800m (35,435ft)
SPAN:	20.11m (66ft)
LENGTH:	18.30m (60ft)
HEIGHT:	unknown
WEIGHT:	loaded 20,000kg (44,092lb)

The first forward-swept wing jet, the Ju 287 V1 was quite successful within its performance levels. Post-war Soviet research with the V1 eventually influenced the Sukhoi S-37.

The Ju 287 V2 had the engines mounted on the wing leading edges as a mass balance, retractable undercarriage and an all-new fuselage.

The V3 would have had a pressurized cabin and operational equipment. It was to be powered by BMW 003 engines, but never flew.

The Ju 287 V1's fuselage was a modified He 177 'Greif' unit, the tail was that of a Ju 388G and the mainwheels came from a Ju 352 transport. The nosewheel came from a crashed or captured B-24 Liberator.

LOCKHEED XF-90 *(1949)*

The XF-90 was an almost unrecognizable relative of the P-80 Shooting Star, designed as a long-range 'penetration fighter' with twin engines and swept wings and tail surfaces. The first of two XF-90 prototypes, 46-687, flew on 4 June 1949, piloted by Tony LeVier without afterburners, and not surprisingly turned out to be underpowered. When afterburners were fitted the designation changed to XF-90A. The programme was terminated in 1950, partly due to the production demands of the Korean War. The first aircraft was tested to destruction in Cleveland. The second aircraft was used to test the effects of nuclear explosions on modern aircraft structures and was placed near ground zero of an atom bomb blast. Surprisingly, the wreck of 46-688 was found in a damaged condition on the Nevada test range in 2003 and is undergoing restoration for the US Air Force Museum.

SPECIFICATIONS (XF-90A)

CREW:	one
POWERPLANT:	two 18.68kN (4200lb-thrust) afterburning Westinghouse J34-WE-11 turbojet engines
MAX SPEED:	1102km/h (685mph)
MAX ALTITUDE:	13,716m (45,000ft)
SPAN:	12.19m (40ft)
LENGTH:	17.10m (56ft 2in)
HEIGHT:	4.82m (15ft 9in)
WEIGHT:	loaded 14,969kg (33,000lb)

The XF-90 lost out in competition against the McDonnell XF-88A, which was subsequently developed as the F-101 Voodoo. More strongly built, but having the same engines, the XF-90 had a poorer performance, and Lockheed's factories were needed for building F-80s for service in the Korean War.

A very unusual feature of the
XF-90 was that the entire vertical
tailfin could be tilted backwards
and forwards to adjust the trim
of the horizontal stabilizer.

The XF-90s had six 20mm (0.79in)
cannon, with their ports located three
per side below the engine intakes.
Other proposed armaments were eight
127mm (5in) high-velocity rockets
and up to 908kg (2000lb) of bombs.

The original requirement called for a
delta-winged design and a prototype was
begun in this configuration. Wind tunnel
tests proved it was a flawed design, and it
was scrapped and restarted.

MARTIN MARIETTA X-24 *(1969)*

The USAF Flight Development Laboratory (FDL) sponsored the X-24 in a parallel programme to NASA's HL-10 and M2 efforts. The aim was again to determine the optimum shape for a manned re-entry vehicle. For its flight trials, the one X-24A built (66-13551) was carried to altitude and dropped by a B-52B mothership. After that it would fire its engine and climb for 2.5 minutes, reaching Mach 1.6 and 21,336m (70,000ft) before beginning a five-minute gliding descent to landing. During the programme that lasted from the first gliding drop test on 17 April 1969 to the 28th (and last) flight on 4 June 1971, the X-24A proved that a lifting body aircraft could make accurate glide landings from near the edge of the atmosphere. The X-24A was modified into X-24B configuration.

SPECIFICATIONS

CREW:	one
POWERPLANT:	one 37.72kN (8480lb-thrust) Reaction Motors (Thiokol) XLR11-RM-13 rocket motor and two 2.24kN (500lb-thrust) auxiliary rockets
MAX SPEED:	Mach 1.55 (1036mph)
MAX ALTITUDE:	21,760m (71,400ft)
SPAN:	4.17m (13ft 8in)
LENGTH:	7.47m (24ft 6in)
HEIGHT:	3.14m (10ft 4in)
WEIGHT:	gross 5194kg (11,450lb)

The X-24 was lenticular (lens-shaped), and this proved a suitable shape for a re-entry vehicle. The X-24's configuration was used again for the unmanned X-38 'space life-boat' tested in 1998.

Control was effected by the two rudders and four large flaps mounted between the outer and central fins. The USAF's Jerauld Gentry and NASA's John Menke made the majority of X-24A flights.

Much of the internal space in the X-24A was taken up by a two large tanks, one for the fuel and the other for oxidizer.

As well as the main rocket engine, the X-24A had two small auxiliary rockets, which could be used to increase the lift during gliding descents. They were also used during high-speed taxi tests prior to the first flight.

The X-24 was preceded by two jet-powered aircraft called the SV-5J, although neither of these actually flew. One was modified to resemble the X-24A for display purposes for the USAF Museum.

MARTIN MARIETTA X-24B (1973)

Following the success of the X-24A, the Flight Dynamics Laboratory (FDL) wanted to refine the aerodynamics of lifting body aircraft with a view towards a future spaceplane design. The so-called FDL-8 configuration proved the most promising, and it was decided that modifying the X-24A was the best way to achieve this. The modifications were extensive, seeing an all-new nose blending into a highly swept wing grafted onto the X-24A. In X-24B configuration, the aircraft flew again on 1 August 1973. John Manke made the first flight and 16 of the subsequent 35. Other X-24B pilots included future space shuttle pilot Francis Scobee. The final tests before the programme ended in September 1975 involved landings to a predetermined runway heading, and these were of great benefit to the space shuttle.

SPECIFICATIONS

CREW:	one
POWERPLANT:	one 43.59kN (9800lb-thrust) Reaction Motors (Thiokol) XLR11-RM-13 rocket motor and two 2.24kN (500lb-thrust) auxiliary rockets
MAX SPEED:	1863km/h (1158mph)
MAX ALTITUDE:	22,595m (74,132ft)
SPAN:	5.84m (19ft 2in)
LENGTH:	11.43m (37ft 6in)
HEIGHT:	3.14m (10ft 4in)
WEIGHT:	6260kg (13,800lb)

The X-24B became the last of the rocket-powered X-planes to fly, and its final 1975 flight marked the end of an era at Edwards Air Force Base. It was nearly a decade before another high-performance aircraft joined the X-series.

Studies were made into an enlarged version designated the X-24C. This would have been built by Lockheed and be capable of flight up to Mach 8, but this programme was cancelled in 1977.

The X-24B had the same XLR-11 engine as the X-24A, although it had higher operating chamber pressures, giving an extra 5.87kN (1320lb-thrust).

Compared to the X-24A, the nose landing gear was moved forward and a new nosewheel designed to take account of the X-24B's greater length and higher gross weight.

MARTIN XB-48 *(1947)*

Martin's XB-48 was one of four manufacturers' designs built to a 1944 USAAF requirement for a medium bomber. Before it was complete, it became clear that Boeing had access to and made use of German aerodynamic research and was building its XB-47 Stratojet with a swept wing.

Two XB-48s were built, the first of them much too heavy and the second longer but within its weight target. Pilots Pat Tibbs and 'Dutch' Galvin made the first flight on 14 June 1947. The drag of the engines was more than predicted (described as 'like a brick wall') and the XB-47 was clearly superior. In September 1948 the Stratojet was ordered instead. In an effort to revive the programme, a turboprop version was proposed with four XT40 turboprops, but by now the USAF was interested only in jets. The second XB-48 kept flying until 1951 on various tests, before it was destroyed in weapons experiments.

SPECIFICATIONS (first aircraft)

CREW:	three
POWERPLANT:	six 16.7kN (3750lb-thrust) Chevrolet J35-C7 turbojet engines
MAX SPEED:	830km/h (516mph)
MAX ALTITUDE:	13,106m (43,000ft)
SPAN:	33.02m (108ft 4in)
LENGTH:	26.14m (85ft 9in)
HEIGHT:	8.08m (26ft 6in)
WEIGHT:	loaded 46,539kg (102,600lb)

Like the Boeing B-47, the XB-48 was a six-engined, high-winged design with a bicycle undercarriage layout. Unfortunately it had straight wings and lower performance.

The two pilots sat in tandem under the bubble canopy. A bombardier/navigator was stationed in the nose.

The bomb bay was able to carry one 9979kg (22,000lb) 'grand slam' bomb or fourteen 454kg (1000lb) bombs on short-range missions.

The XB-48 had a bicycle undercarriage with outrigger wheels at the wingtips. The mainwheel layout was tested on a modified B-26 called the 'Middle River Stump Jumper'.

The thin wings were optimized for high speed and had no room for the retracted undercarriage, hence the bicycle layout.

MCDONNELL XP-67 (1944)

The XP-67, sometimes known as the Bat, was the first fighter built by the McDonnell Aircraft Corporation. In order to reduce drag and aid lift, extensive use of airfoil section fairings was made, with the engines in particular blended into the rest of the airframe. Flight tests began on 6 January 1944, but were delayed by engine problems. On one flight the engines overspeeded and burned out the bearings. Modifications to the tailplane and other parts were necessary, and the XP-67 spent much of its short career in McDonnell's workshops. Flight tests resumed in March, but the Bat exhibited some unpleasant handling characteristics and its performance was not up to expectations. A fire on 6 September 1944 caused serious damage and the prototype was not repaired, nor was the second XP-67 completed.

SPECIFICATIONS

CREW:	one
POWERPLANT:	two 1007kW (1350hp) turbo-supercharged Continental XI-1430-17/1 piston engined
MAX SPEED:	652km/h (405mph)
MAX ALTITUDE:	11,278m (37,000ft)
SPAN:	16.76m (55ft 0in)
LENGTH:	12.80m (42ft 0in)
HEIGHT:	4.51m (14ft 9in)
WEIGHT:	loaded 10,845kg (23,910lb)

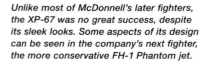

Unlike most of McDonnell's later fighters, the XP-67 was no great success, despite its sleek looks. Some aspects of its design can be seen in the company's next fighter, the more conservative FH-1 Phantom jet.

The XP-67 was intended to have a pressurized cockpit for high-altitude operation, although this was never actually fitted.

A heavy armament was planned for the XP-67, including six 12.7mm (0.50in) machine guns and four 20mm (0.79in) cannon. An alternative suggestion was six 37mm (1.46in) cannon.

The exhausts of the tightly cowled turbo-supercharged engines were configured to give a degree of jet assist. The engines, however, suffered from fires and never gave the rated horsepower.

MIKOYAN-GUREVICH MIG 1.44 *(2000)*

In the early 1980s studies were begun into a 'fifth generation' combat aircraft able to counter the upcoming US Advanced Tactical Fighter, which later became the F/A-22 Raptor. Production contracts for two MFI (multi-functional fighter) prototypes were signed with Mikoyan in 1986. The former USSR's economic and political collapse greatly hampered the project. Originally planned to fly in 1992, the sole MiG 1.44 to actually be built was only rolled out (secretly) and taxi tested in 1994, and finally flown by Vladimir Gorbunov on 15 February 2000. The 1.44 is a technology demonstrator, somewhat simpler than the proposed fighter, which would be designated 1.42. This, it is claimed, would be faster than any likely opposing aircraft. With decreasing likelihood of any production contract, Mikoyan is regarding the 1.44 as a flying laboratory perfecting technologies for future combat aircraft. Photographs of the MiG 1.44 were only released in 1995, and little has been seen of it since other than some images of its first flight. There is no government backing for continued development and little spare company money.

SPECIFICATIONS

CREW:	one
POWERPLANT:	two 196.1kN (44,090lb-thrust) Saturn (Lyul'ka) AL-41F afterburning turbofan engines
MAX SPEED:	2765km/h (1718mph)
MAX ALTITUDE:	unknown
SPAN:	15.50m (50ft 11in)
LENGTH:	20.70m (67ft 11in)
HEIGHT:	5.21m (17ft 1in)
WEIGHT:	maximum 35,000kg (77,160lb)

The 1.44 is optimized for air combat. The large canards, flat underside and flat nose profile are designed to all add to the lift of the wings, particularly at high angles of attack.

Curved intake tunnels prevent the front fans of the engine being seen from a head-on aspect. This also reduces the radar signature.

The 1.44 is a large fighter, with a greater length and wingspan than an F-15 Eagle. Its maximum loaded weight is more than 4000kg (8818lb) greater than that of an F-15C.

MILES M.35 AND M.39B LIBELLULA (1942)

The Miles Aircraft Company mainly built trainers for the RAF, but the Miles Brothers, George and Freddie, were never short of radical ideas. One was the M.35 Libellula (Dragonfly), designed by George and built within eight weeks as a potential carrier-based fighter.

It was developed in private and some secrecy, avoiding wind tunnel tests that would have required Air Ministry approval. George Miles himself made the first flight on 1 May 1942, and the M.35 immediately proved terribly unstable in pitch. Use of ballast only partly cured the problem. The M.39B was a twin-engined machine of the same configuration, built to five-eighths the size of the planned M.39 bomber. It also proved unstable and, although evaluated by the RAF, it failed to lead to a production aircraft of this type, nor any of the airliners mooted by Miles after World War II.

SPECIFICATIONS

CREW:	one
POWERPLANT:	one 97kW (130hp) DH Gipsy Major I Series I inline piston engine
MAX SPEED:	unknown
MAX ALTITUDE:	unknown
SPAN:	6.32m (20ft 5in)
LENGTH:	6.19m (20ft 4in)
HEIGHT:	unknown
WEIGHT:	loaded 839kg (1850lb)

The tandem wing Libellulas offered a wider centre of gravity range than traditional designs. Unfortunately this made achieving stability very difficult, particularly without wind tunnel data.

The M.39B could be considered to have canard foreplanes in the mould of the Eurofighter Typhoon, but the M.35 was more of a tandem wing design with the forward wing only 12.7cm (5in) shorter than the rear wing.

The M.35 was a very basic machine with an open cockpit and only a low-powered engine. The more sophisticated M.39B had two engines driving tractor propellers.

The M.35 had a three wheel fixed undercarriage and was later fitted with an additional tail bumper wheel to protect the pusher propeller on take-off and landing.

NASA/AMES AD-1 *(1979)*

The theories of variable-geometry (swing wings) for high speed flight were understood since the 1940s, but in the 1970s NASA commissioned an aircraft to explore the 'slew wing' theory. This proposed that slewing a wing on a pivot up to 60 degrees gave much lower drag and allowed for low take-off and landing speeds when in the normal position. Burt Rutan had a hand in designing the AD-1 (named for Ames and Dryden, the two NASA research centres behind its development). Coincidentally, the aircraft was built by the Ames Industrial Company of Bohemia, New York. A very simple aircraft of composite construction with two tiny jet engines, the AD-1 cost only $240,000. The wing was slewed by two electric motors and moved at three degrees per second. On 21 December 1979, Tom McMurtry made the first flight in the AD-1. It flew on until August 1982 and proved successful, although no follow-on high-speed aircraft was built.

SPECIFICATIONS

CREW:	one
POWERPLANT:	two 0.98kN (220lb-thrust) Microturbo TRS-18-046 turbojet engines
MAX SPEED:	408km/h (253mph)
MAX ALTITUDE:	unknown
SPAN:	unswept 9.85m (32ft 4in)
LENGTH:	11.82m (38ft 9in)
HEIGHT:	1.98m (6ft 6in)
WEIGHT:	loaded 809kg (1780lb)

The slew wing as tested on the AD-1 promised to offer the same advantages as a swing wing, but with less complexity. The application was considered for a future supersonic airliner, but the AD-1 remains a one-off.

The AD-1's structure was a glassfibre bonded foam core with layers of fabric for strength. Up to 36 layers were used in some places.

The engines were a pair of extremely small turbojets, mounted in external pods attached to the fuselage under the wing centre section.

The tricycle undercarriage was fixed, but mounted very close to the fuselage to give as little drag as possible.

NORD 1400/1402/1405 GERFAUT (1954)

Designed by the French firm Arsenal, which merged with Avions Nord, the ungainly looking Gerfaut was one of Europe's first supersonic aircraft. Arsenal was particularly interested in delta wings and designed an extremely thin wing with a sweepback of 58 degrees.

The Nord 140A Gerfaut with a 27.58kN (6200lb-thrust) Atar 101D engine flew on 15 January 1954 and in August became the first aircraft to exceed Mach 1 in level flight without an afterburner or rocket boost.

The Gerfaut I was followed by the 1402 Gerfaut IB with a larger wing and the 1405 Gerfaut II, which flew in April 1956 and set a range of time to climb records in February 1957. The Gerfaut II, which was said to have 80 per cent revised parts was also used for ground radar trials and to make supersonic missile firings.

**SPECIFICATIONS
(1405 Gerfaut II)**

CREW:	one
POWERPLANT:	one 43.15kN (9700lb-thrust) Atar 10tG-2 afterburninbg turbojet engine
MAX SPEED:	1140km/h (708mph)
MAX ALTITUDE:	5400m (17,717ft)
SPAN:	7.50m (24ft 7in)
LENGTH:	11.39m (37ft 4in)
HEIGHT:	unknown
WEIGHT:	take-off 5250kg (11,574lb)

The tubby Gerfauts were faster than their looks suggested. They were just one of many programmes that did not progress beyond the prototype stage due to the superiority of Dassault's Mirage deltas.

Although capable of supersonic flight without an afterburner, a Nord-designed unit was later fitted to the 1402 and the 1405 was equipped with one from the start.

The Gerfaut's thin delta wing was also used on the Nord Griffon. The thickness-chord ration was only 5.5 per cent.

The straight-through intake duct was unimpeded by the cockpit tub or fuel tanks, which were mounted in a separate structure in the humped upper fuselage.

NORTHROP (AVION) FLYING WING (1928)

As early as 1923, Jack Northrop, then working for Douglas, became fascinated with the idea of all-wing aircraft. In 1928 he left to form the Avion Corporation and created his first such machine, a stressed-metal monoplane having two seats mounted in a thick wing centre section rather than a fuselage. Not quite ready to risk a pure flying wing, Northrop's creation, dubbed 'The Wing', had a small tailplane and endplate fins at the end of two long, thin tailbooms. These were set at an angle to keep the tailplane out of the prop wash. Freelance test pilot Eddie Bellande made the first flight in 1928, flying from Burbank, California, to the Muroc dry lake where testing could be conducted with greater secrecy. Various configuration changes, including relocating the propeller from front to rear, were made and The Wing flew on into 1930.

SPECIFICATIONS

CREW:	one
POWERPLANT:	one 67kW (90hp) Menasco inline piston engine
MAX SPEED:	unknown
MAX ALTITUDE:	unknown
SPAN:	9.30m (30ft 6in)
LENGTH:	6.01m (20ft 0in)
HEIGHT:	1.52m (5ft 0in)
WEIGHT:	unknown

Avion's 'The Wing' was Jack Northrop's first tentative step towards a pure flying wing. It proved pleasant and safe to fly, but the concept was not developed further until Northrop was able to form his own entirely separate company in 1939.

290

The pusher propeller was connected to the Menasco engine by a long extension shaft. This combination gave cooling problems and later the engine was changed for a Cirrus engine and a tractor propeller.

The undercarriage was an unusual 'reverse tricycle' design. The rear wheel was close to the two mainwheels and nearly as large. All wheels were non retractable.

Although a two-seater, The Wing was almost always flown solo and the right-hand cockpit was usually faired over to preserve the airflow characteristics.

NORTHROP HL-10 *(1966)*

Research into the best shape for a space re-entry vehicle saw several NASA-sponsored aircraft reach the flight stage in the late 1960s, including the NASA M2-F1 and Northrop M2-F2, and the USAF's Martin X-24 lifting body designs. The highest-performing of all these was Northrop's HL-10. The designation was comprised of HL for 'horizontal landing' and 10 for it being the 10th configuration of a series of model studies. Bruce Peterson made the first of the HL-10 flights on 22 December 1966. The first 11 flights were all unpowered glides, with the lifting body dropped from a height of 13,716m (45,000ft) from a pylon under a B-52. The first powered flight was not until October 1968. With rockets fired, the HL-10 climbed to altitude and simulated the approach path of a space vehicle, taking six to seven minutes to glide to a landing on a dry lake bed.

SPECIFICATIONS

CREW:	one
POWERPLANT:	one 35.7kN (8000lb-thrust) Reaction Motors XLR-11 rocket engine
MAX SPEED:	1976km/h (1228mph)
MAX ALTITUDE:	27,524m (90,303ft)
SPAN:	4.15m (13ft 7in)
LENGTH:	6.45m (21ft 2in)
HEIGHT:	2.92m (9ft 7in)
WEIGHT:	loaded 2721kg (6000lb)

Although designated outside of the X-plane series, the HL-10 pushed the boundaries of lifting body flight for NASA to (literally) new heights. It proved useful for the Space Shuttle and other programmes, and today is displayed at the NASA Dryden facility.

The rocket engine was the famous XLR-11, used on the X-1 and other rocket planes for more than 20 years. It had four chambers, which could be fired together or independently to give differing amounts of power.

The transparent nosecone allowed the pilot to keep the runway in sight during the high-angle of attack landing approach. The landing required a dive and a 'flare-out' procedure to obtain the correct angle just before touchdown.

The HL-10's nose landing gear came from a T-39 Sabreliner, the main gear was from a T-38 trainer and the ejection seat was modified from that of an F-106.

NORTHROP N-1M AND N-9M (1940)

By 1939 Jack Northrop was able to concentrate on the creation of a true flying wing based on new aerodynamic research since the original 'Wing' of 1929. The new Northrop Aircraft Company built the N-1M as a private venture research vehicle. The odd designation stood for Northrop Model 1 Mock-up, although it was not a mock-up in the traditional sense.

Vance Breese made the first flight of the N-1M on 3 July 1940. Despite its wood and steel tube construction, the N-1M was overweight and underpowered, but made more than 200 flights, proving the flying wing concept. Northrop convinced the Defense Department to commission the N-9M as a one-third scale testbed for their proposed B-35 flying wing bomber. The first of four was flown by John Myers on 27 December 1942. It was lost in a crash in March 1943, but the programme carried on, with the aircraft proving excellent pilot trainers for the B-35 and B-49 bombers.

SPECIFICATIONS (N-1M)

CREW:	one
POWERPLANT:	two 48kW (65hp) Lycoming O-145 inline piston engines
MAX SPEED:	322km/h (200mph)
MAX ALTITUDE:	1219m (4000ft)
SPAN:	11.6m (38ft 0in)
LENGTH:	5.2m (17ft 0in)
HEIGHT:	1.5m (5ft 0in)
WEIGHT:	empty 1814kg (4000lb)

The N-1M and N-9M were the first real ancestors of the B-2 stealth bomber. Today the N-1M is in the National Air and Space Museum collection; the surviving N-9MB was restored in the 1990s and today flies as part of the Planes of Fame collection.

The N-1M was very adjustable. The wingtips were originally drooped, with ailerons also acting as rudders. The tip angle could be adjusted on the ground. By exchanging various sections, the wing sweep, twist, dihedral and span could all be adjusted between flights.

Elevons on the trailing edges filled the roles of both elevators and ailerons. Rudder functions were achieved with split flaps at the wingtips. Similar devices were used on all the larger flying wings, including the B-2.

The fourth N-9MB had 90kW (120hp) Franklin 0-540-7 engines rather than the Menasco Pirate motors used on the others and was designated the N-9MB.

NORTHROP X-21A (1963)

Two Douglas WB-66D Destroyers were modified by Northrop into X-21As to explore Laminar Flow Control (LFC) theory. This proposed that great efficiencies could be achieved by sucking air into slots on the upper wing surface to maintain a laminar airflow throughout the flight envelope. Both aircraft were test-flown by Jack Wells: 55-0408 on 18 April 1963 and 55-0410 on 15 August. The B-66 airframe was not ideal compared with a purpose-built airframe. Laminar flow could not be achieved on every flight and was affected by turbulence, precipitation, dust, dirt, humidity and flying through cloud. Keeping the slots clean was difficult and probably would have been impractical on an operational LFC aircraft in squadron service.

SPECIFICATIONS

CREW:	five
POWERPLANT:	two 41.81kN (9400lb-thrust) General Electric J79-GE-13 turbojet engines
MAX SPEED:	901km/h (560mph)
MAX ALTITUDE:	12,954m (42,500ft)
SPAN:	28.50m (93ft 6in)
LENGTH:	22.94m (75ft 3in)
HEIGHT:	7.80m (25ft 7in)
WEIGHT:	loaded 37,648kg (83,000lb)

The X-21A programme suffered several delays for technical reasons and was cancelled due to budget pressures in 1965. It proved that Laminar Flow Control was not really suitable for combat aircraft.

The wing surfaces of the X-21A contained long slots, which had more than 800,000 tiny holes within them. Compressors under the wing pulled in the air for a suction effect to keep the airflow in contact with the surface. At best, 95 per cent laminar flow was achieved.

The B-66's arrangement of underslung J57 engines was replaced by two non-afterburning J79s mounted on the rear fuselage to keep the wing as aerodynamically clean as possible.

Both X-21As were put into storage at Edwards Air Force Base,California, and became semi-derelict. The remains may be combined to create a single display airframe.

NORTHROP X-4 BANTAM *(1948)*

The X-4 Bantam was designed to explore the transonic region of the flight envelope. Some aerodynamicists had the theory that by leaving off the horizontal tail that instability caused by the shock wave would be eliminated. Northrop had much experience of tailless designs so was chosen to build the two X-4s. The No. 1 aircraft was first flown by Charles Tucker on 16 December 1948 and, between the two machines, the X-4 made 112 flights up to September 1953. Porpoising and tucking under were among the phenomena uncovered by test flights that reached up to Mach 0.94. Chuck Yeager was one of the pilots hired by Northrop for the initial acceptance tests and flew the X-4 eight times. Another famous pilot, Scott Crossfield, flew the Bantams 31 times for NACA. Both X-4s survive, one at the US Air Force Museum and the other at the Air Force Academy in Colorado Springs.

SPECIFICATIONS

CREW:	one
POWERPLANT:	two 7.12kN (1600lb-thrust) Westinghouse XJ-30 turbojet engines
MAX SPEED:	1030km/h (640mph)
MAX ALTITUDE:	13,411m (44,000ft)
SPAN:	8.18m (26ft 10in)
LENGTH:	7.10m (23ft 3in)
HEIGHT:	4.54m (14ft 10in)
WEIGHT:	unknown

The main achievement of the X-4 was to prove that swept-wing aircraft without horizontal tails were not suitable for transonic and supersonic flight. Various forms of instability manifested themselves as the X-4 approached Mach 1.

The wing mounted split flaps doubled as powerful airbrakes. Some tests of asymmetric flap operation were made to test their effect on transonic trim and control forces.

The X-4 was the first of the X-series to be fitted with an ejection seat, and was also the first as a conventional bubble canopy.

The X-4s had an endurance of only 44 minutes. A 284-litre (75-gallon) external fuel tank was fitted for some flights in an attempt to improve this.

6676

USAF

SCALED COMPOSITES ARES *(1990)*

The US Army dabbled with jets in the 1950s and 1960s, but US Air Force opposition restricted them to helicopters and transports. The idea of an 'organic' fixed-wing close air support aircraft was revived with the Scaled Composites ARES (Agile-Response Effective Support) designed by Burt Rutan. The ARES first flew on 19 February 1990, piloted by Doug Shane. The ARES was literally built around a General Electric GAU-12 25mm (0.98in) cannon that dictated the asymmetric layout of the compact airframe, which was largely made of carbon-fibre over a foam/PVC core. After USAF evaluation, it was used to test some systems for private manufacturers and remained available for commercial testbed purposes. It appeared in the appalling 1992 film *Iron Eagle III* portraying a 'Me 263'.

SPECIFICATIONS

CREW:	one
POWERPLANT:	one 13.12kN (2950lb-thrust) Pratt and Whitney Canada JT15D-5 turbofan engine
MAX SPEED:	750km/h (466mph)
MAX ALTITUDE:	unknown
SPAN:	10.67m (35ft 0in)
LENGTH:	8.97m (25ft 5in)
HEIGHT:	3.00m (9ft 10in)
WEIGHT:	maximum 2767kg (6100lb)

A 1981 Army request for a Low Cost Battlefield Attack Aircraft (LCBAA) requirement was eventually met by the Scaled Composites Model 151, or ARES. Despite a promising test programme, no further development took place.

The engine was offset to the left by eight degrees and the fuselage was mounted to the right of the wing centreline. This was partly to balance the weight of the heavy cannon and also to keep gun gases from being ingested into the engine.

The small size and composite construction contributed to the ARES's stealth, as did the location of the tailbooms, which shielded the jet efflux from infrared sensors.

The canard foreplane is something of a Rutan trademark and helped contribute to the low stalling speed of the ARES. The forward-swept canard design was unusual, however.

SUD-EST SE.2410 GROGNARD (1950)

One of the many French jet designs that reached the hardware stage in the decade after the end of World War II was the single-seat attack aircraft called the Grognard ('Grumbler'). The name was one applied to Napoleon's Old Guard soldiers. The first prototype SE.2410 flew on 30 April 1950 and the second, which was designated the SE.2415 and called the Grognard II, in February 1951. This version, which had reduced wing sweep, suffered from tailplane flutter and was damaged in a belly landing, which was made after a false fire warning. Development of a Tay-engined SE.2418 production version got under way, but the Sud-Ouest Vautour II was more advanced and was accepted for production as the Armée de l'Air's new medium bomber and night-fighter.

SPECIFICATIONS (Grognard I)

CREW:	one
POWERPLANT:	two 21.53kN (4850lb-thrust) Hispano-Suiza Nene 101 turbojet engines
MAX SPEED:	1038km/h (645mph)
MAX ALTITUDE:	service ceiling 11,582m (38,000ft)
SPAN:	12.58m (44ft 6.5in)
LENGTH:	15.39m (50ft 6in)
HEIGHT:	unknown
WEIGHT:	loaded 14,500kg (31,967lb)

The humpbacked Grognard had an unusual internal layout of two stacked engines fed by a single dorsal intake. It was not a very elegant design and was passed over in favour of the Vautour with podded engines and a bubble canopy.

The engines were mounted one above the other in the rear fuselage, as on the English Electric Lightning. The jet flow exited out of a single outlet at the tail.

The two prototypes were unarmed, but the proposed production version would have been armed with two internal 30mm (1.18in) DEFA cannon and bombs or rockets.

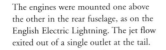

The wings were swept at 47 degrees on the Grognard I and at 32 degrees on the Grognard II.

SUKHOI S-37/SU-47 BERKUT *(1997)*

The Grumman X-29 influenced the Sukhoi design team in the early 1980s when it was exploring configurations for the proposed 'fifth-generation' fighter demanded by the Soviet hierarchy. Known by the company project designation S-37 and the product designation Su-47, Sukhoi's response was begun after the MiG 1.44, but was publicly revealed and flew well before its Mikoyan competitor. The details of the Su-47 Berkut (Golden Eagle) were almost totally unknown outside Russia until Igor Votintsev made the first flight on 25 September 1997. Although having many superficial similarities to the Su-27 'Flanker' series, the Su-47 is almost all new. Most notable is its forward-swept wing, which is a largely composite construction to prevent aeroelastic twisting. It draws inspiration not just from the X-29, but also from the Tsybin LL-2 of 1947 and before that the Junkers 287 bomber. Budget problems make it unlikely that a service version will ever appear.

SPECIFICATIONS

CREW:	one
POWERPLANT:	two 122.58kN (27,557lb-thrust) NPO Saturn (Lyul'ka) AL-31F afterburning turbofan engines
MAX SPEED:	1700km/h (1057mph)
MAX ALTITUDE:	unknown
SPAN:	16.70m (54ft 10in)
LENGTH:	74ft 2in (22.6m)
HEIGHT:	6.36m (20ft
WEIGHT:	loaded 24,000kg (52,910lb)

Like the MiG 1.44, the S-37/Su-47 has been overtaken by developments elsewhere. It is likely to serve as a testbed for technologies intended for the new Russian 'PAK-FA' fighter programme.

Aerodynamically, the Su-47 is sometimes described as a 'triplane', having a canard, a wing and a tailplane. The future addition of vectoring nozzles may add an extra level of control.

The outer wing is swept forward at 40 degrees on the trailing edge and 24 degrees on the leading edge. The short-span, long-chord tailplanes have a leading-edge sweepback angle of 75 degrees

SUPERMARINE 510 (1948)

The Supermarine 510 was evolved from the Attacker naval fighter to become the first British jet with a swept wing and tail surfaces.

Mike Lithgow made the initial flight of VV106 at Boscombe Down on 29 December 1948. It was soon discovered that fully powered controls would be needed to maintain control in pitch and yaw at higher speeds with a swept-wing craft. In November 1950 VV106 became the first swept-wing aircraft to make a landing and take-off from an aircraft carrier, HMS *Illustrious*. After a wheels-up landing the 510 was rebuilt as the Type 517 with a hinged rear fuselage, which moved with the tailplane as a trimming device. In this configuration it was flown until 1995. Today it is preserved at the Fleet Air Arm Museum at Yeovilton, Somerset.

SPECIFICATIONS

CREW:	one
POWERPLANT:	one 22.24kN (5000lb-thrust) Rolls-Royce Nene 2 turbojet engine
MAX SPEED:	1062km/h (660mph)
MAX ALTITUDE:	unknown
SPAN:	9.69m (31ft 9in)
LENGTH:	11.59m (38ft 1in)
HEIGHT:	2.71m (8ft 10in)
WEIGHT:	loaded 5523kg (12,177lb)

Britain's swept-wing fighter development was later than that in the USA, USSR and even Sweden. The 510 was a cautious step towards the RAF's first British swept-wing fighter, the Supermarine Swift.

For its carrier trials the 510 was fitted with an arrester hook and bridles for catapult launching. A blunt nose replaced the pointed unit originally used and most of the undercarriage doors were replaced.

The 510/517 retained many features of the Attacker carrier fighter, including the twin tailwheels and 'elephant ear' intakes.

The taildragger layout was not popular with test pilots and was replaced with a more conventional nosewheel layout in the Swift. Its advantage was that it gave a higher angle of incidence and thus shorter take-off run.

SUPERMARINE 525 (1954)

The Supermarine 525 stemmed from the first British efforts to produce a purpose-built carrier-based jet fighter. The Type 505 had a butterfly or V tail, and was expected to belly land on a rubber 'flex deck'. When this idea was abandoned it was revised as the Type 508 with a conventional undercarriage. During construction the third prototype Type 508 (VX138) was modified with a swept wing with an average (mid-chord) sweep of 50 degrees and swept tail surfaces. Flying on 27 April 1954, the Type 525 proved only slightly faster than the 508, with a lower climb rate. The solution was seen as applying the 'area rule' to the fuselage and making various wing and tail modifications. The 525 was lost after going into a spin in July 1955 and a whole new aircraft, the Type 544 with a dogtooth leading edge, was built to carry on the test programme.

SPECIFICATIONS

CREW:	one
POWERPLANT:	two 33.36kN (7500lb-thrust) Rolls-Royce R.A.7 turbojet engines
MAX SPEED:	1040km/h (646mph)
MAX ALTITUDE:	unknown
SPAN:	11.31m (37ft 2in)
LENGTH:	16.15m (53ft 0in)
HEIGHT:	4.54m (14ft 11in)
WEIGHT:	loaded 9031kg (19,910lb)

The short-lived Supermarine 525, by way of the Type 544, led to the Scimitar carrier fighter, the first production British swept-wing naval fighter.

The tailfin as originally built was considered inadequate in area. Some modifications were made to the tip area. A range of air scoops and vents were added to the upper fuselage at the same time.

The wing tanks were only in the inboard sections and the outer wing structure was designed to allow wing folding, although the mechanism was never fitted.

Compared to the 508, the 525's new wing was set much further forward. The undercarriage legs were also considerably longer.

ROYAL NAVY VX138

TSYBIN LL *(1947)*

In September 1945 the little-known design bureau of V.N. Tsybin was tasked with creating a research aircraft for transonic flight. Another bureau (Beresnev) was studying wing configurations, and in the end Tsybin's solid fuel rocket aircraft, the Ts-1, was built in three forms, designated the LL (flying laboratory) -1, -2 and -3. The LL-1 had straight wings like the X-1 and flew 30 times from mid-1947, the first time with M. Ivanov at the controls. The LL-2 had 40-degree rearward swept wings with 12 degrees dihedral, but never actually flew. The most radical was the LL-3 with 30-degree forward-swept wings and considerable dihedral. The LL-3 flew 100 times in the hands of four pilots. It was towed to height by a Tu-2 bomber, flew under rocket power for 8-10 seconds, then landed as a glider.

SPECIFICATIONS (LL-3)

CREW:	one
POWERPLANT:	one 14.71kN (3307lb-thrust) Kartukov PRD-1500 solid-fuel rocket motor
MAX SPEED:	1200km/h (746mph)
MAX ALTITUDE:	unknown
SPAN:	7.22m (23ft 8in)
LENGTH:	8.98m (29ft 6in)
HEIGHT:	unknown
WEIGHT:	loaded 2039kg (4495lb)

The Russian equivalent to the X-1, the Tsybin LLs reached speeds of up to only Mach 0.97, but advanced the state of high-speed research in the USSR. The short duration burn of the rocket motor was a handicap.

The Tsybin LL series aircraft were mainly wooden in construction. The forward-swept wings of the LL-3 were metal. Faster speeds than those achieved might have led to structural failure from aeroelastic twisting.

There were only two airframes in the LL programme. The straight-wing LL-1 was refitted with a swept wing to become the LL-2. Other (jet) swept-wing jet designs were providing enough useful data at the time.

Water tanks were used to balance the aircraft when test instrumentation was not fitted. This was dumped through valves before the LLs made a skid landing.

TUPOLEV VAKHMISTROV ZVENO (1931)

Soviet designer Vladimir Vakhmistrov developed the parasite aircraft concept as a method of extending the range of fighter aircraft. It developed through various forms until successfully used to launch fighter-bombers in World War II. The first 'Zveno' (Link) combination comprised a Tupolev twin-engined TB-1 mother-ship and two specially modified Tupolev I-4 fighters. The Zveno-1 flew on 3 December 1931 with A.I. Zelevsky piloting the TB-1 and V. Chkalov and A. Anisimov flying the fighters. The Zveno-1a was a TB-1 carrying two larger I-5 biplane fighters. Developments continued using a TB-3 bomber, which was essentially a four-engined scaled up TB-1. The Zveno-2 carried three I-5s, one of them on the fuselage top. The ultimate expression of the parasite concept was the Aviamatika (Mother Aircraft), which flew with no fewer than six aircraft of four types attached.

SPECIFICATIONS (TB-3)

CREW:	eight to ten
POWERPLANT:	four 611kW (916hp) Mikulin AM-34RN piston engines
MAX SPEED:	245km/h (152mph)
MAX ALTITUDE:	7740m (25,394lb)
SPAN:	39.5m (129ft 6in)
LENGTH:	24.4m (79ft 10in)
HEIGHT:	unknown
WEIGHT:	empty 11,417kg (25,170lb)

The extraordinary Zveno combinations were a uniquely Soviet solution to patrolling large areas of airspace. A later version using I-16 monoplanes saw combat in 1941 and was responsible for the destruction of a vital bridge.

A careful launch sequence was followed to release the fighters symmetrically. On the first release the bomber's co-pilot made a mistake and one fighter remained attached for some time without ill effects.

The Zveno-1 had two fighters mounted above the wings. Getting the fighters aboard the Zveno-1 required them to be hauled up wooden rails to the wing's top surface using manpower.

All sorts of experiments with the Zveno combinations were made, including attaching and detaching the fighters in flight or making take-offs with the fighters attached, supplying extra power with their own motors.

A supercritical wing reverses the shape of the standard aerofoil in that the top surface is flat and the lower surface is curved. This allows cruising near Mach 1 without buffeting and gives better low-speed handling characteristics. This had applications for airliner design – it was said that a large airline would save many millions of dollars in fuel costs each year through improved efficiency.

An F-8A Crusader was chosen for NASA's supercritical wing (SCW) programme largely because of its high wing, which could easily be replaced. Rockwell fabricated the new wing in 1969, and the F-8 was modified at NASA's Dryden Flight Research Center at Edwards Air Force Base, California. The first SCW flight took place on 9 March 1971 with Tom McMurtry at the controls. The programme demonstrated that the SCW wing was 15 per cent more efficient in the transonic regime than a standard wing.

SPECIFICATIONS

CREW:	one
POWERPLANT:	one 64.50kN (14,500lb-thrust) Pratt & Whitney J57-P-12 afterburning turbojet engine
MAX SPEED:	unknown
MAX ALTITUDE:	unknown
SPAN:	13.12m (43ft 1in)
LENGTH:	16.5m (54ft 3in)
HEIGHT:	4.8m (15ft 9in)
WEIGHT:	loaded approx 15,464kg (34,100lb)

The SCW programme provided useful data about wing efficiency, but ended in 1973. Airline manufacturers did not adopt supercritical wing designs.

The supercritical wing is flatter on the top and rounder on the bottom, with a downward curve at the trailing edge. This delays the onset of the supersonic shock wave, giving less drag and a better ride at transonic speeds.

The original wingspan of the F-8A was 10.70m (35ft 2in), while the wingspan with the supercritical wing was 13.12m (43ft 1in).

NASA

810

FLIGHT RESEARCH CENTER

SUPERCRITICAL WING

There was only one F-8 (SCW) modified, although NASA used other Crusaders, including one (NASA 816) fitted with a digital fly-by-wire control system. The F-8 (SCW) NASA 810 is displayed today outside the Dryden Flight Research Center in California.

WESTLAND PTERODACTYLS (1928)

Professor Geoffrey Hill was a proponent of safe, stall-proof aircraft and built several gliders before joining Westland in 1926. There he built a series of aircraft sharing the name Pterodactyl, beginning with the Pterodactyl I in 1928. The proposed Mk II and III fighters were skipped in favour of the Pterodactyl IV research aircraft that first flew in June 1931. This also suffered from unwanted porpoising movement. The definitive Mk V with a tractor engine was built to an Air Ministry specification and flew for the first time in May 1934. It was intended as a fighter with forward guns and a gunner behind the pilot with a clear field of fire for his Lewis gun. Proving nearly as unstable as its predecessors and slower than its contemporaries, the Mk V ensured that the programme did not last long.

SPECIFICATIONS
(Pterodactyl V)

CREW:	one
POWERPLANT:	one 447kW (600hp) Rolls-Royce PV.G Goshawk piston engine
MAX SPEED:	306km/h (165mph)
MAX ALTITUDE:	unknown
SPAN:	14.22m (46ft 8in)
LENGTH:	6.96m (22ft 10in)
HEIGHT:	unknown
WEIGHT:	loaded 2313kg (5100lb)

The extraordinary Pterodactyls were certainly ahead of their time. They were also inferior to even the biplanes of their day and were not developed into service aircraft. Only the Pterodactyl I survives, on display in the Science Museum, London.

The Pterodactyl I had a 52kW (70hp) Armstrong Siddeley Genet motor, the Mk IV an 89kW (120hp) de Havilland Gypsy III and the Mk V a 447kW (600hp) Rolls-Royce P.V.G, later named Goshawk. The particular engine in the Mk V suffered from poor reliability.

The Mk V had a design weakness in the wing, which was uncovered when the left wing collapsed during taxiing trials on a rough airfield. This delayed the first flight by 18 months.

The unique undercarriage on the Pterodactyl V included mainwheels in a bicycle arrangement with two more tiny wheels on outrigger arms attached to the lower stub wings.

Index

Picture Credits